California
Everyday
Mathematics

English Learners Handbook

Grade **1**

McGraw Hill **Wright Group**

The McGraw-Hill Companies

EL Consultant
Elizabeth Jiménez

Photo Credits
© Ralph A. Clevenger/Corbis, cover, *center*; © Getty Images, cover, *bottom left*;
© Tom & Dee Ann McCarthy/Corbis, cover, *right*.

www.WrightGroup.com

 **Wright Group**

Printed in the United States of America.

Send all inquiries to:
Wright Group/McGraw-Hill
P.O. Box 812960
Chicago, IL 60681

ISBN 978-0-07-612885-3

MHID 0-07-612885-7

2 3 4 6 7 8 9   MAL   13 12 11 10 09 08

The McGraw·Hill Companies

Contents

Unit 5

Unit 6

Unit 7

Introduction

This handbook is intended as a support guide to help California teachers of English Learners use *Everyday Mathematics*® to meet the rigorous California Mathematics Content Standards. *Everyday Mathematics* incorporates Universal Access instructional strategies to enhance student comprehension and to promote the generalization and transfer of skills and knowledge. The *English Learners Handbook* provides a wide variety of recommendations on lesson delivery to make the grade-level concepts more accessible while maintaining the rigorous mathematics of the program.

Everyday Mathematics English Learners Handbook is designed to provide access to the core mathematics curriculum in two important ways—to create access to concept instruction through instructional delivery that maximizes understanding and to accelerate the acquisition of academic language pertinent to each lesson. The support lessons also address the California English Language Development Test (CELDT) levels of proficiency and California English Language Arts Standards to ensure that English Learners are fully prepared to meet the standards as assessed by the CELDT, the California Standards Test (CST), and eventually the California High School Exit Examination (CAHSEE).

California's English Learners

California's classrooms welcome children, speaking over one hundred different languages, from all around the world. English Learners in California enter the classroom with many similarities and differences in languages spoken at home, previous school preparation, and academic background in English. This means that teachers have a tremendous opportunity to enrich the learning of all by drawing on children's prior knowledge and experiences, which will yield a wealth of information for teachers, parents, and children to build upon. The challenge of such differences means that teachers need support materials that accelerate learning, that maintain the rigorous content of the program, and that help them check the understanding of all children.

This handbook helps teachers meet the needs of their diverse classrooms by recognizing that grade level does not dictate English proficiency. For example, English Learners in higher grade levels may be at beginning English proficiency levels if they are recent arrivals. Conversely, children in the early grades may be at higher levels of English proficiency. Some English Learners have extensive educational background, which includes the study of English. Others may have very limited formal school experiences, which may mean they lack literacy skills in their home language and English. Support lessons include instruction to make the mathematics accessible and the language comprehensible.

Using the Support Lessons

For each instructional lesson in *Everyday Mathematics*, this handbook provides a support lesson to help teachers meet the specific needs of English Learners. Because Progress Check lessons assess skills learned, they do not have a corresponding support lesson.

Providing Access recommends proven instructional-delivery strategies to maximize English Learners' comprehension of math concepts.

Previewing Vocabulary lists words with multiple meanings, key math terms, common procedural vocabulary, or idiomatic phrases that are used in the lesson and explanations of the word meanings to clarify and build support for the mathematics.

Building Academic Language focuses on and develops academic language based on the specific math skill taught in each lesson.

Checking for Understanding provides examples of prompts that can be used to monitor English Learners' comprehension of lesson content at the first three proficiency levels established by the CELDT.

Lesson 1·2 Investigating the Number Line

Providing Access: Sharing Cultural Access
Using rhymes, songs, and chants from games provides children with new vocabulary, language repetition, and rhythm, which adds predictability. Often, the rhymes and games children know are based on their cultural background. Introduce these songs and games when they are used in the lessons so all children become familiar with them. In this lesson, the game Simon Says may be new to English Learners.

Previewing Vocabulary
An explanation of words with multiple meanings, key math terms, and common procedural vocabulary may aid student comprehension. Consider previewing these terms and reinforcing them as they are used in the lesson.

Words and Phrases	Meanings
mystery number, page 21	A mystery is something that is unknown. A mystery number is a number that is not known.
greater than, page 21	*Greater than* means bigger than or more than, which is different from the meaning of *great* in "You did a great job!"
absent, page 22	Explain that a child not at school that day is absent.

Building Academic Language: Comparatives and Superlatives
As children play the *Monster Squeeze Game,* they may need help with the clues given in the game. Introduce the pattern for forming comparison words, draw a simple chart, and ask children to contribute to it.

Positives	Comparatives	Superlatives
big	bigger	biggest
small	smaller	smallest

Checking for Understanding
Use the prompts below, your own questions, and the master on page 110 to plan comprehension checks for English Learners.

English Proficiency	Prompts
Beginning	*During* Monster Squeeze, *use gestures to show if your number is smaller than (less than) or more than (bigger than or greater than) _____.*
Early Intermediate	*Is 4 more than or less than 3?*
Intermediate	*Give clues using "greater than" and "less than" to find the number on the number line.*

2   *EL Handbook*

Providing Access

In much the same way that *Everyday Mathematics* embraces the requirement of the *Mathematics Framework for California Public Schools* to anticipate, identify, address, and correct children's common errors and misconceptions in mathematics, the support lessons in this handbook address potential linguistic challenges for English Learners. Each support lesson begins with a Providing Access section which offers . . .

◆ An example of one of the challenges that teachers of English Learners may face

◆ An approach to making the mathematics accessible to children at all English language proficiency levels

◆ An additional way to support the *Mathematics Framework for California Public Schools* Category 5 requirement for instructional planning and support

The following activities illustrate instructional methods found in the Providing Access section of each support lesson.

Flexible Grouping

The *Mathematics Framework for California Public Schools* chapter on Universal Access recommends various grouping strategies for English Learners, such as working in small groups. Small-group activities give children an opportunity to practice English in context and support comprehension as children can easily ask for clarification. Children who speak the same home language may deepen their comprehension of concepts by sharing and clarifying their understanding, and then transferring their learning to English.

Using Visuals

As the mathematics concepts become more complex, the level of abstraction and the academic complexity of the language children need to discuss the concepts increase. Using visuals along with verbal explanations strengthens children's comprehension. Look for ways to support concepts with visuals and encourage English Learners to demonstrate their understanding by adding visuals to their answers.

Using Reference Materials

Encourage English Learners to use reference materials, such as encyclopedias, almanacs, and dictionaries (including bilingual dictionaries). Note that many of the words in the unit vocabulary list are similar to the Spanish words, which may enhance Spanish speakers' retention of new terminology. List the following English and Spanish words for children: *angle/ángulo, circle/círculo, parallel/paralelo, interior/interior,* and *polygon/polígono.*

Using Diagrams to Solve Problems

It is often challenging to practice abstract concepts or higher-level thinking questions when children have limited English proficiency. Use graphic organizers, such as the parts-and-total diagram, to engage English Learners in critical thinking without heavily increasing the linguistic demand. Have children of Beginning English proficiency work with a partner. Remind them to refer to the Guide to Solving Number Stories for help.

Using Structured Routines

Routines are built into *Everyday Mathematics* to help children work efficiently and effectively. Routines support better comprehension for English Learners because the predictability allows them to listen more closely to the new concept rather than having to focus on the procedural information.

Role-Playing

An excellent way to deepen understanding of concepts is to give children the opportunity to apply what they have learned to a familiar situation. In a Grade 3 lesson, a shopping trip is simulated, using the Stock-Up Sale Posters (to provide visual references) and play money as a manipulative (to help children practice making change). Have English Learners take turns being the shopkeeper and the customer. This role play helps children learn and practice the phrases and vocabulary they need when handling money in real situations.

Tapping Prior Knowledge

English Learners sometimes feel that they must rely on others to help them understand the instruction and practice in school each day. Working with metric measurement presents an excellent opportunity for English Learners to share their expertise with the group. Those who have gone to school outside the United States may know the metric system well. Explore this asset in your class and utilize any metric experts.

Using Gestures

One way to reinforce the meaning of instructions is to use gestures to emphasize a phrase or word. In one lesson, children talk about clockwise and counterclockwise turns. Establish a gesture with children to reinforce each direction.

Using Graphic Organizers

One way for English Learners of limited proficiency to work with rigorous content is to use graphic organizers. A Venn diagram, flow chart, storyboard, or sequence chart allows children to fill in vital information and show their understanding without having to use extensive language. In this lesson, have children use a Venn diagram to compare and contrast the attributes of different quadrangles. Brainstorm the attributes together.

Previewing Vocabulary

English Learners often encounter words used in English that impede their understanding of new math concepts. The purpose of previewing vocabulary is to bring to the teacher's attention vocabulary that is integral to understanding the lesson. These words generally are . . .

◆ Words that may be misunderstood because they differ from their everyday meanings or are being used as different parts of speech, such as to estimate (v.) and an estimate (n.)

◆ Collocations, which are phrases that use a word in multiple ways, such as *right on, right away, Bill of Rights,* and *right-side*

◆ Idioms, which are expressions that are not predictable from the usual meaning of the words, for example, *as the crow flies*

◆ Cultural terms that English Learners may not be familiar with, such as *zip code, area code, leap year,* and so on

The following illustrates the features of the Previewing Vocabulary section. In the left-hand column of the table are the words and the page numbers on which they occur in the *Teacher's Lesson Guide*. Sometimes a word appears on a student page within the lesson. If that is the case, then the student page is listed in the right-hand column. The Meanings are to help the teacher describe the words to children, but are not meant to be word-for-word definitions.

Words and Phrases	Meanings
plan, page 199	(v.) In A Guide for Solving Number Stories, *plan* means to make a strategy or *plan*.
carry out, page 199	The expression *carry out* is a collocation that means to put a plan into action and follow it through to its completion. (See p. 175 in the *Student Reference Book*.)
look back, page 200	The expression *look back* means to review or to go back and check over your work to be sure it is correct.

Key Vocabulary

Note that along with the Previewing Vocabulary section in each support lesson of the *English Learners Handbook,* lessons in *Everyday Mathematics* identify Key Vocabulary. Children are encouraged to use this vocabulary in meaningful ways throughout the lesson to develop a command of mathematical language. Key Vocabulary is identified in the following places:

◆ In the Unit Organizer of the *Teacher's Lesson Guide*

◆ On each lesson opener in the *Teacher's Lesson Guide*

◆ Throughout the lesson in boldface print when the words are first introduced

◆ In the glossary of the *Teacher's Lesson Guide*

Building Academic Language

The Mathematics Framework for California Public Schools addresses the wide diversity of needs in many California classrooms, including children in benchmark, strategic, and intensive groups. Chapter 6 on Universal Access calls for instructional materials that are designed to help all children attain grade-level math standards and accelerate the acquisition of academic language.

Everyday Mathematics English Learners Handbook stresses the development of academic language. The Building Academic Language section includes mathematics terminology and the grammar, syntax, phonemic awareness, pronunciation, or lexicon needed to accelerate the acquisition of academic language.

Academic language refers to language used to express abstract concepts, in contrast to social language, which is used to talk about daily activities. English Learners generally become proficient in conversational English quickly while the acquisition of academic language is often a much slower and less-structured process. Teachers can accelerate children's acquisition of academic language by making it a focus of planning and intentional teaching based on diagnosis of need.

The following pages highlight the content found in the Building Academic Language section of each lesson. Along with a sample of the topics covered in this part of the support lessons, you will find additional information on the specific strategies for building academic language. As you implement the ideas in this part of the support lessons, refer to these pages for examples of charts and further explanation of the language-building strategies.

Academic language includes . . .

◆ Words with multiple meanings

◆ Mathematics terminology, symbols, and related language

◆ Idiomatic expressions

◆ Borrowed words and cognates

◆ Both transferable and nontransferable phonemes, grammar, and written mechanics

Words with Multiple Meanings

Words with multiple meanings are identified in the Previewing Vocabulary section and may be further discussed in the Building Academic Language section. Words with multiple meanings are spelled the same whether they are used as nouns or verbs, but may be pronounced differently based on their use. For example, the word *estimate* can mean "an estimate" or "to estimate." When the word is preceded by an article (*an* or *the*), it is a noun. When preceded by the word *to, estimate* is a verb. These words generally are not the Key Vocabulary found in the lessons, but when explained, they provide greater access to the meaning of the lesson.

Attribute Adjectives

The systematic introduction of description is included to help children of early proficiency levels accelerate their understanding and usage of English. In a lesson in Grade 3, children explore congruent shapes. To help English Learners expand their descriptive vocabulary, the Providing Access section has children create a large four-column chart to capture words that describe attributes.

Size	Shape	Color	Other

Language of Probability

A Providing Access section in Grade 3 has teachers review with English Learners the words and phrases that are associated with probability. They create a three-column chart with the headings: *Sure Will Happen, Uncertain/Not Sure,* and *Sure Will Not Happen,* and decide together where to place the following phrases: *impossible, 50-50 chance, certain, for sure, no way, likely, almost, surely, very likely,* and *improbable.*

Sure Will Happen	Uncertain/Not Sure	Sure Will Not Happen

Idioms and Expressions

Academic language includes expressions that proficient speakers of English use and reference, such as . . .

◆ Sayings

◆ Proverbs

◆ Idioms

◆ Cultural and literary references

Native speakers may acquire this language in social conversation over the course of years. However, in order to accelerate language acquisition for English Learners, teachers need to explain and provide practice with idioms and other such sayings. Encourage English Learners to ask for clarification when idioms are used and the meaning is unclear.

The Building Academic Language section often recommends that children collect words or phrases in a word chart. Word charts consist of a column to collect the specified language concept, a column for children to describe the meaning, and a column for children to illustrate or create a symbol to represent the word or phrase. Below is an example of a word chart for idiomatic expressions used in the lessons.

Word Chart		
Measurement Idioms and Expressions	**Meanings**	**Illustrations**
measure up	To reach a certain standard or to be capable or qualified is to measure up.	
for good measure	Something added, just to be sure, is done for good measure.	
as the crow flies	This phrase means to use the most direct route from point to point on a map.	

The following is an example of a Building Academic Language section on idioms:

Idioms

The English language has many idiomatic expressions. Idioms can be puzzling to even advanced English Learners. As you explain the expression *rule of thumb*, discuss the following idioms and what they mean: *all thumbs* and *to have a green thumb*. When children figure out the total area of their skin, discuss the idioms: *by the skin of his teeth* and *it's no skin off my nose*.

Cognates

An important component of accelerating academic language acquisition for English Learners is teaching strategies for learning new words and concepts in English. Most English Learners begin to acquire English by comparing new words and elements to the language they already know. For children who speak a primary language other than English that shares Greek, Latin, or Arabic roots, there are many prefixes, suffixes, and cognate patterns that they can use to learn new academic English words.

Cognates are words that share roots across languages. They have the same meaning and may be spelled similarly in other languages. The Building Academic Language section of the support lessons specifically points out cognate patterns between English and Spanish. You may want to search the Internet for cognate patterns between English and other languages.

An example of cognates are words that end with *-tion* or *-sion* in English, which share the same root with Spanish words ending in *-ión*, such as the names of the mathematical operations: *addition / adición, subtraction / sustracción, division / división,* and *multiplication / multiplicación.*

The support lessons encourage children to list both the English and Spanish cognates. However, in cases where the English word is spelled exactly the same as the Spanish word, the lesson only specifies listing the English word. When children look for these word patterns, they can more quickly ascertain the meaning of the English word by applying what they know from a related language. Below are a few examples of cognate patterns and cognates in English and Spanish:

	English	Spanish	English	Spanish
Word Ending	-or	-or	-uct	-ucto
Cognate	divisor	divisor	product	producto

	English	Spanish	English	Spanish
Word Ending	-al	-al	-ty	-dad
Cognate	visual	visual	variety	variedad

	English	Spanish	English	Spanish
Word Ending	-ble	-ble	-ic	-ico
Cognate	divisible	divisible	numeric	numérico

Skill Transfer across Languages

The smallest similarity or difference between English and another language is the set of phonemes or sounds that are used to form words. The Building Academic Language section may highlight sounds that may be difficult for children to understand or pronounce in English. For example, Spanish does not have consonant clusters that begin with /s/ in the initial position of words. This means that Spanish speakers may mispronounce the words *school, score, stop, shoe, space, small* and other English words beginning with an *s* consonant cluster. Children may add a vowel before these words to approximate the sound.

Many pronunciation errors are predictable because the sounds do not transfer to English from a child's home language. Below is a segment from a contrastive analysis chart that shows common phonemes. The plus sign shows where the phoneme occurs in English and Spanish words:

Consonants	English			Spanish		
	Initial	Medial	Final	Inicial	Medial	Final
/m/	+	+	+	+	+	-
/s/ includes letter *c*	+	+	+	+	+	+
/t/	+	+	+	+	+	-
/b/	+	+	+	+	+	-
/k/ includes letter *c*	+	+	+	+	+	-

Grammar contrasts are also addressed in Building Academic Language sections. Children may examine related plurals, verb tenses, or related word families. For example, English Learners construct graphic organizers to categorize words with different plural endings in English.

Children must learn not only new English words but the patterns, rules, and exceptions of the language. To support English Learners as they write number stories and explain answers using oral and written language, Building Academic Language sections may provide sentence frames for children to use as they acquire these language skills.

Accelerating academic language takes a strong knowledge of the California Mathematics Content Standards, planning based on the results of diagnosis and assessments, intentional lesson preparation, and skilled instructional delivery.

Checking for Understanding

Checking for understanding is key to helping children accelerate their comprehension. However, this kind of informal assessment must go beyond simply asking children whether they understand.

Each support lesson lists prompts for checking student understanding at different English proficiency levels. Most often the prompts are related to the mathematics of the lesson. Some also involve the related academic language needed to make sense of lesson content. Below is an example of prompts from a lesson in Grade 3:

English Proficiency	Prompts
Beginning	*There are 12 pennies and 3 children. Draw a picture or use pennies to illustrate sharing the pennies equally.*
Early Intermediate	*There are 12 pennies and 3 children. Draw a picture or use pennies to illustrate sharing. How many pennies does each child get if you share equally?*
Intermediate	*There are 12 pennies and 3 children. Draw a picture or use pennies to illustrate sharing. Are there any other solutions possible?*

The following chart shows additional ways to check for understanding appropriate to the child's English proficiency. The prompts in each lesson are built on these leveled statements and are tiered in language demand and complexity to follow the CELDT proficiency descriptors. For English Learners at Early Advanced and Advanced proficiency levels, use the discussion questions that are part of the core lesson. Use the prompts in this section, your own questions, and the master on page 110 to plan comprehension checks for English Learners.

Beginning Proficiency	Early Intermediate Proficiency	Intermediate Proficiency
◆ Thumbs-up/thumbs-down...	◆ Either ____ or ____	◆ Compare/contrast
◆ Nod your head yes/no...	◆ Give a one-word answer or short answer	◆ Describe...
◆ Show me...	◆ Make a list...	◆ Sequence...
◆ Point to the...	◆ Complete a sentence frame or template	◆ How...? or Why...? (open-ended questions)
◆ Illustrate...	◆ Complete a graphic organizer	

Resources

Research-Based Strategies

◆ Provide daily opportunities for students to read, write, and speak in the mathematics lesson (Anstrom 1997).

◆ Connect mathematics to students' life experiences and existing knowledge (Anstrom 1997; Barwell 2003; Secada and De La Cruz 1996).

◆ Create classroom environments rich in language and mathematics content (Anstrom 1997).

◆ Promote active student participation in classroom discussions regarding mathematics (Brenner 1998; Brown, Ash, Rutherford, Nakagawa, Gordon, and Campione 1993).

◆ Model expected behavior (Mather and Chiodo 1994).

◆ Use concrete materials, illustrations, and demonstrations to enhance mathematical learning (Raborn 1995).

◆ Connect language to visual aids such as pictures, tables, and graphs (Khisty and Chval 2002).

◆ Speak key mathematical vocabulary repeatedly within meaningful contexts (Brenner 1998).

◆ Rephrase and emphasize key mathematical ideas and concepts (Khisty and Chval 2002).

◆ Write key ideas, concepts, and words on the board (utilize as much board space as possible so that you do not have to erase during the lesson) (Stigler, Fernandez, and Yoshida 1996).

◆ Listen to students' mathematical thought processes (Secada and De La Cruz 1996).

◆ Model the difference between hearing and listening (Chval 2001).

◆ Encourage students to look at other students while they are speaking (Brown, Ash, Rutherford, Nakagawa, Gordon, and Campione 1993; Rogoff and Toma 1997).

◆ Encourage students to ask questions and respond to their peers in whole-group discussions (Brown, Ash, Rutherford, Nakagawa, Gordon, and Campione 1993; Rogoff and Toma 1997; Secada and De La Cruz 1996).

◆ Emphasize meaning (students may need to communicate meaning through the use of gestures or drawings as they develop command of the English language) (Moll 1988; Moll 1989; Morales, Khisty, and Chval 2003).

References

Anstrom, K. 1997. *Academic achievement for secondary language minority students: Standards, measures, and promising practices*. Washington, DC: National Clearinghouse for Bilingual Education.

Barwell, R. 2003: Patterns of attention in the interaction of a primary school mathematics student with English as an additional language. *Educational Studies in Mathematics* 53 (1): 35–59.

Brenner, M. 1998. Development of mathematical communication in problem solving groups by language minority students. *Bilingual Research Journal* 22 (2, 3, & 4).

Brown, A. L., D. Ash, M. Rutherford, K. Nakagawa, A. Gordon, and J. C. Campione. 1993. Distributed expertise in the classroom. In *Distributed cognitions: Psychological and educational considerations*, ed. G. Salomon, 188–228. New York: Cambridge University Press.

Chval, K. B. 2001. A case study of a teacher who uses calculators to guide her students to successful learning in mathematics. PhD diss. University of Illinois at Chicago.

Khisty, L. L., and K. Chval. 2002. Pedagogic discourse and equity in mathematics: When teachers' talk matters. *Mathematics Education Research Journal* 14 (3): 154–168.

Mather, J., and J. Chiodo. 1994. A mathematical problem: How do we teach mathematics to LEP elementary students? *The Journal of Educational Issues of Language Minority Students* 13: 1–12.

Moll, L. 1988. Key issues in teaching Latino students. *Language Arts* 65 (5): 465–472.

Moll, L. 1989. Teaching second-language students: A Vygotskian perspective. In *Richness in writing: Empowering ESL students*, eds. D. Johnson and D. Roen, 55–69. New York: Longman.

Morales, H., L. L. Khisty, and K. Chval. 2003, July. Beyond discourse: A multimodal perspective of learning mathematics in a multilingual context. In *Proceedings of the 2003 Joint Meeting of PME and PMENA,* ed. N. Pateman, 3: 133–140. Honolulu: Center for Research and Development Group, University of Hawaii.

Raborn, D. T. 1995. Mathematics for students with learning disabilities from language-minority backgrounds: Recommendations for teaching. *New York State Association for Bilingual Education Journal* 10, 25–33.

Rogoff, B., and C. Toma. 1997. Shared thinking: Community and institutional variations. *Discourse Processes* 23: 471–491.

Secada, W. G., and Y. De La Cruz. 1996. Teaching mathematics for understanding to bilingual students. *Binational Programs Meeting the Needs of Migrant Students: A Handbook for Teachers and Administrators*, ed. J. L. Flores, 285–308. ERIC Clearinghouse on Rural Education and Small Schools.

Stigler, J. W., C. Fernandez, and M. Yoshida. 1996. Traditions of school mathematics in Japanese and American elementary classrooms. In *Theories of mathematical learning*, eds. L. P. Steffe, P. Nesher, P. Cobb, G. A. Goldin, and B. Creer, 149–175. Mahwah, NJ: Lawrence Erlbaum Associates.

Providing Access: Labeling the Room

Label all visual routines in the room. For example, display the word *Calendar* above the calendar and *Number Line* over the Class Number Line. Displaying the written words next to the actual item provides English Learners with a reference they can use when working on journal pages and during discussions.

Previewing Vocabulary

An explanation of words with multiple meanings, key math terms, and common procedural vocabulary may aid student comprehension. Consider previewing these terms and reinforcing them as they are used in the lesson.

Words and Phrases	Meanings
job, page 18	Work that a person does on a regular basis is a job. Tell children: *I am a teacher; that is my job. You are a student; that is your job.*
straw, page 18	A small plastic tube used for drinking is a *straw*. Straws are sometimes white but also come in different colors. Some children may know that *straw* is used to feed animals.
coins, page 18	Coins are small, round, metal discs called *money*. Pennies, dimes, nickels, and quarters are all coins. Each coin has a different value.
Day Counter, page 18	Day Counter is a classroom job; the person tells the number of days that you have been in school.

Building Academic Language: Changing Verbs to Nouns

Explain to children that one way to describe people who do a job is to add *er* to the end of the word that tells what they do. For example, a person who teaches is a teacher. A person who runs is a runner. In this lesson, a person who counts days is a Day Counter. Make a chart of jobs that fit this pattern and have children add to it: *A person who ____ is a ____.*

Checking for Understanding

Use the prompts below, your own questions, and the master on page 110 to plan comprehension checks for English Learners.

English Proficiency	Prompts
Beginning	Walk to the calendar. Point to the label. *Does this say calendar?*
Early Intermediate	Point to the calendar. *Is this the calendar or the number line?*
Intermediate	*Name three things that make this a calendar.*

Investigating the Number Line

Providing Access: Sharing Cultural Access

Using rhymes, songs, and chants from games provides children with new vocabulary, language repetition, and rhythm, which adds predictability. Often, the rhymes and games children know are based on their cultural background. Introduce these songs and games when they are used in the lessons so all children become familiar with them. In this lesson, the game Simon Says may be new to English Learners.

Previewing Vocabulary

An explanation of words with multiple meanings, key math terms, and common procedural vocabulary may aid student comprehension. Consider previewing these terms and reinforcing them as they are used in the lesson.

Words and Phrases	Meanings
mystery number, page 21	A mystery is something that is unknown. A mystery number is a number that is not known.
greater than, page 21	*Greater than* means bigger than or more than, which is different from the meaning of *great* in "You did a great job!"
absent, page 22	Explain that a child not at school that day is absent.

Building Academic Language: Comparatives and Superlatives

As children play the *Monster Squeeze Game,* they may need help with the clues given in the game. Introduce the pattern for forming comparison words, draw a simple chart, and ask children to contribute to it.

Positives	Comparatives	Superlatives
big	bigger	biggest
small	smaller	smallest

Checking for Understanding

Use the prompts below, your own questions, and the master on page 110 to plan comprehension checks for English Learners.

English Proficiency	Prompts
Beginning	*During* Monster Squeeze, *use gestures to show if your number is smaller than (less than) or more than (bigger than or greater than)* _____.
Early Intermediate	*Is 4 more than or less than 3?*
Intermediate	*Give clues using "greater than" and "less than" to find the number on the number line.*

Providing Access: Sharing Cultural Expectations

In this lesson, children work with a partner. Children who speak different home languages often differ in their expectations of working with others. For example, some languages employ different pronouns to express polite language. Because English does not have different pronouns to show respect, politeness is shown in different ways, such as waiting for others to finish speaking, making eye contact, and asking questions to show interest. Review the phrases "thank you," "please," and "you are welcome."

Previewing Vocabulary

An explanation of words with multiple meanings, key math terms, and common procedural vocabulary may aid student comprehension. Consider previewing these terms and reinforcing them as they are used in the lesson.

Words and Phrases	Meanings
tool kit, page 26	A box or collection of tools that can be used for building things or making repairs is a tool kit. The tool kits children use in *Everyday Mathematics* are small bags that they keep their materials in.
lost and found, page 26	A lost and found is a place where everyone agrees to put any items (e.g. hats, mittens, or lunch boxes) that are found so that they can be returned to the person who lost them.

Building Academic Language: Tapping Vocabulary Knowledge

Draw a large circle around the word *tools*. Connect four or five smaller circles with subtopics to *tools*; for example, cooking tools, tools for writing, tools for building and repairing, and tools for mathematics. Assign a different subtopic to each small group to brainstorm tools in that category. Record children's responses on the word web.

Checking for Understanding

Use the prompts below, your own questions, and the master on page 110 to plan comprehension checks for English Learners.

English Proficiency	Prompts
Beginning	*Show me the ruler. Point to the number line with the ruler.*
Early Intermediate	*Which of these is not a tool for mathematics: a calculator, a desk, or a ruler?*
Intermediate	*Choose one math tool and describe how it is used.*

Number-Writing Practice

Providing Access: Routines for Comprehension

Routines are built into *Everyday Mathematics* to help children work efficiently and effectively. Routines support comprehension by providing predictability, which allows English Learners to focus on the new concept rather than the procedural information.

Previewing Vocabulary

An explanation of words with multiple meanings, key math terms, and common procedural vocabulary may aid student comprehension. Consider previewing these terms and reinforcing them as they are used in the lesson.

Words and Phrases	Meanings
How old were you _____?, page 30	Explain that this question asks about a person's age.
What number comes after _____?, page 30	Explain that this question is used to ask about numbers in order.
shaving cream, page 31	Shaving cream is a soft, white soap cream that comes in a can, used during shaving.

Building Academic Language: Describing Age

In this lesson, children are asked to share their ages. In English, a person says, "I am _____ years old." In Spanish, speakers say, "I have _____ years." Anticipate that children may make errors describing age based on the structure of their home language. Also note that not all cultures count age in the same way. Some consider children a year old when they are born. During this discussion, let children know that it is considered impolite to ask adults their age.

Checking for Understanding

Use the prompts below, your own questions, and the master on page 110 to plan comprehension checks for English Learners.

English Proficiency	Prompts
Beginning	*Stand up when I call out your age. 1...2...3...4...5...6...*
Early Intermediate	*I am going to guess your age. Say "older" if you are older than the number I say. 1...2...3...4...5...6...*
Intermediate	*Ask the student next to you, "How old are you?"*

Providing Access: Role-Playing

English Learners may benefit from role-playing the actions in a number story. The use of physical actions reinforces the meaning of the number story and allows the teacher to assess children's understanding. Watching others role-play also aids comprehension.

Previewing Vocabulary

An explanation of words with multiple meanings, key math terms, and common procedural vocabulary may aid student comprehension. Consider previewing these terms and reinforcing them as they are used in the lesson.

Words and Phrases	Meanings
shortcut, page 35	A route or a way to get some place that takes less time or distance is a shortcut.
bunny, page 35	A bunny is a baby or young rabbit. Many animals have different names for their babies; for example, dogs have puppies.
bakery, page 35	A shop where people make and sell baked goods, such as cookies, cakes, and bread, is a bakery.
best numbers, page 36	Explain that the numbers that children write that most resemble the model numbers are their best numbers. During number-writing practice, children are asked to circle their best numbers.

Building Academic Language: Collocations

English Learners may know the word *count* but may not know the meaning of some phrases that use *count*. For example, the word *off* in "count off by threes" does not convey the everyday meaning of *off*. These phrases are known as *collocations*. In this lesson, children *count up* and *count back*. Have children create a simple book of math phrases with the word *count* and illustrate the meaning of each phrase.

Checking for Understanding

Use the prompts below, your own questions, and the master on page 110 to plan comprehension checks for English Learners.

English Proficiency	Prompts
Beginning	Show thumbs-up if I am counting up, thumbs-down if I am counting back. 1, 2, 3, 4, 5…
Early Intermediate	When I count, tell me if I am counting up or counting down. 5, 4, 3, 2, 1.
Intermediate	With a partner, count up from 1 to 10.

Providing Access: Playing Games

An excellent strategy to use with English Learners is to practice new math skills through games. Playing games provides language practice and uses repetition without creating boredom. In this lesson, the game *Top-It* is introduced; children review greater than and less than with *Monster Squeeze* and count and compare numbers by playing the *Penny-Dice Game*.

Previewing Vocabulary

An explanation of words with multiple meanings, key math terms, and common procedural vocabulary may aid student comprehension. Consider previewing these terms and reinforcing them as they are used in the lesson.

Words and Phrases	Meanings
ordering, page 38	To put numbers in order is called *ordering*.
facing up, page 39	Explain that when you lie on your back, your face is looking up. When a number card is faceup, the side with the numbers is showing.
exit slip, page 39	*Exit* means to leave. Here, the word *slip* means a small piece of paper.
counters, page 41	These are small objects used to help keep track of counting numbers. Children may remember that the Day Counter (Lesson 1.1) is a person who counts the days.

Building Academic Language: Understanding Idioms

As English Learners progress to higher levels of English proficiency, English expressions can continue to be a challenge because they often carry assumed cultural knowledge. In this lesson, children connect the dots. In everyday English, the expression *connect the dots* is sometimes applied to situations where a clear picture is formed by following simple clues.

Checking for Understanding

Use the prompts below, your own questions, and the master on page 110 to plan comprehension checks for English Learners.

English Proficiency	Prompts
Beginning	*Use counters to show me a number that is more than 3.*
Early Intermediate	*Is 2 more than 3? Is 2 less than 3?*
Intermediate	*Grab two handfuls of counters and line up each handful. Explain how to match the counters to show which handful has more.*

Recording Tally Counts

Providing Access: Using Graphic Organizers

In this lesson, children make a tally chart to count their pets. Explain that because the total number keeps changing, a tally chart is a better way of recording the number than writing a number and continually erasing or crossing it out.

Previewing Vocabulary

An explanation of words with multiple meanings, key math terms, and common procedural vocabulary may aid student comprehension. Consider previewing these terms and reinforcing them as they are used in the lesson.

Words and Phrases	Meanings
pets, page 44	Animals that live with people in their homes are pets and are different from farm animals and wild animals. Examples of pets are dogs, cats, fish, birds, and turtles.
whisper, page 45	To speak in a very soft voice so others cannot hear what you are saying is to whisper.
Circle the best number, page 45	(v.) To circle is to draw a line around something, forming a circle. Here the word *circle* is an action.

Building Academic Language: Nontransferable Skill—*ll*

Not all letter sounds are the same across languages. The double *l* in *tally* is pronounced like a single *l* sound. In Spanish the letter *ll* is pronounced as /y/. Point out that in English whether there is one or two *l*'s in a word, single or double *l* is pronounced /l/.

Checking for Understanding

Use the prompts below, your own questions, and the master on page 110 to plan comprehension checks for English Learners.

English Proficiency	Prompts
Beginning	*Draw a picture of your favorite pet.*
Early Intermediate	*Name a pet you have. Name a pet you would like to have.*
Intermediate	*Are there more tally marks for pets owned than children in your class? Why?*

Investigating Equally Likely Outcomes

Providing Access: Sharing Cultural Access

Rhymes, chants, and songs provide children with new vocabulary, language repetition, and rhythm, which adds predictability. Often the rhymes children know are based on their cultural background so it is important to introduce these rhymes to English Learners. In this lesson, children learn Rock, Paper, Scissors.

Previewing Vocabulary

An explanation of words with multiple meanings, key math terms, and common procedural vocabulary may aid student comprehension. Consider previewing these terms and reinforcing them as they are used in the lesson.

Words and Phrases	Meanings
round, page 50	(n.) A round in a game is the name for the periods, episodes, or the turns back and forth between players.
tie, page 50	When both players end a game with the same score, it is called a *tie* or a *tied game*.

Building Academic Language: Words with Multiple Meanings

As English Learners expand their proficiency in English they will encounter many words with everyday meanings they know but have different meanings in math. Make a chart listing the words *match, tie game, second round,* and *sheet of paper*. Have children add others and illustrate each word or phrase to remember how the term is used in math.

Checking for Understanding

Use the prompts below, your own questions, and the master on page 110 to plan comprehension checks for English Learners.

English Proficiency	Prompts
Beginning	*Demonstrate Rock, Paper, Scissors.*
Early Intermediate	*Tell who won the round of Rock, Paper, Scissors.*
Intermediate	*Explain why the winner won the round of Rock, Paper, Scissors.*

Lesson 1·9
The Calendar

Providing Access: Using Real Objects

Help English Learners tackle new concepts and vocabulary by tying new words to real objects (realia) or visual representations. In this lesson, children learn about the calendar by using a real calendar. This strategy strengthens the connection between the word and the concept. If possible, find a wall calendar from a local business. Ask students why they think some businesses give away calendars for free.

Previewing Vocabulary

An explanation of words with multiple meanings, key math terms, and common procedural vocabulary may aid student comprehension. Consider previewing these terms and reinforcing them as they are used in the lesson.

Words and Phrases	Meanings
keep track, page 53	To keep some kind of record of is to keep track of something.
date, page 53	The date is the calendar number. Help English Learners distinguish between *date* and *day*, for example, Monday.
up to today, page 53	This expression includes what has happened until today. In this lesson, children fill in the missing dates from the beginning of the month up to today.
school holidays, page 54	Days when school is not in session, usually to celebrate or commemorate a special event or occasion, are school holidays.

Building Academic Language: Future Tense

Using the calendar provides a context for practicing questions about when an event will take place and gives English Learners practice using the future tense. For example, ask children when vacation will begin.

Checking for Understanding

Use the prompts below, your own questions, and the master on page 110 to plan comprehension checks for English Learners.

English Proficiency	Prompts
Beginning	*Point to the day that your homework is due.*
Early Intermediate	*When will vacation begin? In how many days will you celebrate your birthday?*
Intermediate	*Ask another student to name the days of the week that school is in session.*

Providing Access: Flexible Grouping

Working in small groups gives children an opportunity to practice English in context and supports comprehension through collaborative work. Children who speak the same home language may deepen their comprehension of concepts through sharing and clarifying their understanding with one another.

Previewing Vocabulary

An explanation of words with multiple meanings, key math terms, and common procedural vocabulary may aid student comprehension. Consider previewing these terms and reinforcing them as they are used in the lesson.

Words and Phrases	Meanings
facedown, page 57	Explain that when you lie down on your stomach, your face is down and people cannot see who you are. When cards are facedown, you cannot see the numbers.
scratch paper, page 58	Paper that may be used to write calculations on but is not turned in for review is scratch paper. In this expression, *scratch* means that the paper might have cross outs and erasures on it.
counters, page 59	Counters are small objects, often round plastic discs, that are used by children to keep track of their counting.

Building Academic Language: Imperative Form

In this lesson, children learn the expectations for working in small groups. Rules for behavior are often posted and described in commands, such as "Use quiet voices," "Be polite," "Share materials" and "Take turns." Note that some English Learners may misunderstand the command to "behave" as two separate words, *be* and *hāve*.

Checking for Understanding

Use the prompts below, your own questions, and the master on page 110 to plan comprehension checks for English Learners.

English Proficiency	Prompts
Beginning	*With your hands, demonstrate larger and smaller. Show on the number line a number smaller than 3.*
Early Intermediate	*Point to a number on the number line and say whether it is larger or smaller than 4.*
Intermediate	*Explain how you know that this number is larger than 3.*

Lesson 1·11

Explorations: Exploring Math Materials

Providing Access: Connecting Mathematics to Everyday Life

In this lesson, children explore patterns. Have children work in small groups to find patterns in the classroom, on their clothing, as well as on the clock, calendar, and so on. Ask children to select a pattern they like best and draw it. Post their drawings on the bulletin board and discuss the characteristics of the designs, such as repetition and color.

Previewing Vocabulary

An explanation of words with multiple meanings, key math terms, and common procedural vocabulary may aid student comprehension. Consider previewing these terms and reinforcing them as they are used in the lesson.

Words and Phrases	Meanings
attribute, page 61	A characteristic of an object is an attribute.
match, page 63	Explain that to match numbers or objects, you pair up two objects that share characteristics.
pick, page 63	To select or to choose is to pick.

Building Academic Language: Cognates

Mathematics is rich with terminology rooted in Greek and Latin. English Learners who speak a language that shares these roots may benefit from reviewing cognates or related words. For example, the following English words that end with -tion share a common root with Spanish words ending in -ión: exploration/exploración, addition/adición, education/educación. Have children listen for other -tion words in the lesson.

Checking for Understanding

Use the prompts below, your own questions, and the master on page 110 to plan comprehension checks for English Learners.

English Proficiency	Prompts
Beginning	Find a pattern in the classroom and point to each part of the pattern.
Early Intermediate	Name the colors in this pattern in order.
Intermediate	Name the attributes in the pattern you like best. Describe the shape, color, number...

Providing Access: Seasons in California

Identifying the subtle changing of seasons in some regions of California can be a challenge for children who have lived in very different climate regions. Ask for members of the class familiar with the region's weather to report the weather. Invite children to help the Weather Person by sharing words that describe snow, sunny weather, rain, and fog.

Previewing Vocabulary

An explanation of words with multiple meanings, key math terms, and common procedural vocabulary may aid student comprehension. Consider previewing these terms and reinforcing them as they are used in the lesson.

Words and Phrases	Meanings
weather person, page 65	A weather person, usually a reporter on television or radio, reports the daily weather and predicts the weather for the coming week. The Weather Person is a job in Grade 1.
set a temperature, page 69	Explain that when you want the heater or air conditioner to keep the room at a certain temperature, you set the thermostat at that temperature.
hunt, page 69	To search for someone or something is to hunt.
word bank, page 70	A collection of words and their meanings is a word bank.

Building Academic Language: Talking about the Weather

Help English Learners of early proficiency levels talk about the daily temperature by using sentence frames. Encourage children to use phrases such as "between ____ and ____ degrees Fahrenheit," "almost ____ degrees Fahrenheit," and "about halfway between ____ and ____ degrees Fahrenheit."

Checking for Understanding

Use the prompts below, your own questions, and the master on page 110 to plan comprehension checks for English Learners.

English Proficiency	Prompts
Beginning	*Do you like hot weather? Do you like cold weather? Point to a cold temperature on the thermometer.*
Early Intermediate	*Say the name of each of the weather symbols.*
Intermediate	*What is your favorite kind of weather? Why?*

Number Stories

Providing Access: Expanding Vocabulary

In this lesson, number stories involve animals, including puppies. Discuss common animal names as well as the words for their offspring to build vocabulary. Discuss the following examples: dogs/puppies, cats/kittens, and lions/cubs. Then make a two-column chart for children to complete, listing the names of other adult animals and their babies.

Previewing Vocabulary

An explanation of words with multiple meanings, key math terms, and common procedural vocabulary may aid student comprehension. Consider previewing these terms and reinforcing them as they are used in the lesson.

Words and Phrases	Meanings
[a] die, page 74	(n.) One of a pair of dice is a die. Children may try to call the die in the *Penny-Dice Game* "a dice." They may know *die* as a verb.
[to] spy, page 75	(v.) To look for something that may be hidden is to spy.

Building Academic Language: Regular and Irregular Past Tense

When working with number stories, it is helpful to notice the language children must know in order to navigate the mathematics. Create a two-column chart to collect regular past tense verbs that add *-ed*, such as *save/saved*, and those that change the base word to form the past tense, such as *lose/lost*, *give/gave*, and *find/found*.

Checking for Understanding

Use the prompts below, your own questions, and the master on page 110 to plan comprehension checks for English Learners.

English Proficiency	Prompts
Beginning	*Use a storyboard to draw a number story using zoo animals.*
Early Intermediate	*Use a storyboard to draw a number story using zoo animals. Tell the number and name of each animal in your story.*
Intermediate	*Make up a number story about zoo animals. Ask your partner if you need help with a word.*

Number Grids

Providing Access: Modeling to Aid Comprehension

An excellent way for English Learners to deepen their understanding of directional words is through physical movement. For example, in this lesson, children follow directions and hop *forward* or *backward* to a given number on the number line. When possible, have children demonstrate other directional words through movement.

Previewing Vocabulary

An explanation of words with multiple meanings, key math terms, and common procedural vocabulary may aid student comprehension. Consider previewing these terms and reinforcing them as they are used in the lesson.

Words and Phrases	Meanings
markers, page 95	Game pieces for marking a spot on a gameboard are markers.
forward/backward, page 95	Explain that forward is the direction that you see when you look ahead; you face forward. Backward is the direction behind you.
roll the die, page 95	A die is one in a pair of dice. When you roll the die, you toss it so that it rolls, and then comes to a stop.
land, page 96	Explain that in a board game, when a game piece stops and comes to rest on a spot or place, it lands on that place.

Building Academic Language: Collocations

Note that in this lesson on the number grid, the word *count* is used in several phrases to give directions. This can be confusing to English Learners who hear the word *count* used in a number of different ways. Demonstrate the meaning of each phrase, using a transparency or floor number line, to *count up, count back,* and *count backward.* Explain that the word *up* in the phrase *count up* means to count to higher numbers.

Checking for Understanding

Use the prompts below, your own questions, and the master on page 110 to plan comprehension checks for English Learners.

English Proficiency	Prompts
Beginning	*On the number line, demonstrate counting up from 0 to 5.*
Early Intermediate	*Listen to these numbers: 1, 2, 3, 4... Am I counting up or counting backward?*
Intermediate	*Listen to these numbers: 1, 2, 3, 4... Am I counting up or counting backward? How do you know?*

Numbers All Around

Providing Access: Chunking Numbers

In this lesson, children examine familiar numbers, such as addresses, phone numbers, and TV channels. Children learn to chunk long numbers in groups of three or four to make them easier to remember. Explain that phone numbers in other countries are chunked differently, sometimes in groups of two or three. Discuss the advantages of having a 3-digit emergency phone number.

Previewing Vocabulary

An explanation of words with multiple meanings, key math terms, and common procedural vocabulary may aid student comprehension. Consider previewing these terms and reinforcing them as they are used in the lesson.

Words and Phrases	Meanings
everyday life, page 100	This phrase refers to the common, routine activities that most people do every day.
make up, page 100	To make up is to form by putting together. For example, numbers make up a phone number.
area code, page 101	Three digits in a phone number that identify the section or area of the country where the phone is located is the area code.

Building Academic Language: Reading Numbers

Sometimes when people recite a phone number, they call the *zero* in the phone number "oh." Reading telephone numbers in English may be confusing. For example, the area code (209) is read "two, zero, nine" or "two, oh, nine" but not "two hundred and nine." The area code (310) is read "three, one, zero" or "three ten" but not "three hundred ten." Use the word *zero* with children to avoid confusion.

Checking for Understanding

Use the prompts below, your own questions, and the master on page 110 to plan comprehension checks for English Learners.

English Proficiency	Prompts
Beginning	*What is your age? Show me how old you are.*
Early Intermediate	*Is the number 7 someone's age or their phone number?*
Intermediate	*How many numbers are in a telephone number including the area code?*

Complements of 10

Providing Access: Connecting Concepts to Visual Cues

In this lesson, children work with handfuls of pennies. Reinforce *right* and *left* by drawing two large hands on the board and labeling them. Record the number of pennies inside the outlines of each hand. Represent the coins with circles and number each coin as you count it. Have children trace their own hands on paper and cut them out to make visual models to track the pennies they grab.

Previewing Vocabulary

An explanation of words with multiple meanings, key math terms, and common procedural vocabulary may aid student comprehension. Consider previewing these terms and reinforcing them as they are used in the lesson.

Words and Phrases	Meanings
two-fisted, page 105	Explain that when you fold in your fingers, you form a fist. *Two-fisted* means to form fists with both hands like when you grab pennies in Two-Fisted Penny Addition.
handful, page 105	A handful is a small, imprecise quantity or number. It refers to as much as the hand can hold.

Building Academic Language: Cultural Sayings

The expression, "Practice makes perfect," is discussed to introduce how Math Boxes are used. (See *TLG* page 106.) Explain that every language and culture shares its wisdom and values through these short sayings. Ask children to share any sayings or wise expressions about practice. Have children translate if needed. List the expressions on a chart.

Checking for Understanding

Use the prompts below, your own questions, and the master on page 110 to plan comprehension checks for English Learners.

English Proficiency	Prompts
Beginning	*Raise your right hand. Raise your left hand. Demonstrate a fist.*
Early Intermediate	*Complete this phrase, "I have _____ pennies in my right hand. I have _____ pennies in my left hand."*
Intermediate	*In this lesson, we talk about a handful of pennies. Could you say a fistful of pennies? Why or why not?*

Unit Labels for Numbers

Providing Access: Labeling the Room

In an earlier lesson, visual routines in the room, such as the Class Number Line, were labeled. Now, add labels to the storage areas for math tools, such as the calculators, tool kits, and so on. When you display the written words next to the actual items, you provide English Learners with a reference they can use to access these materials on their own. Consider drawing a picture on each word's label to help English Learners decipher the meaning.

Previewing Vocabulary

An explanation of words with multiple meanings, key math terms, and common procedural vocabulary may aid student comprehension. Consider previewing these terms and reinforcing them as they are used in the lesson.

Words and Phrases	Meanings
key, page 111	A key is a part that is pressed by a finger, as in the key on a calculator, computer, or piano. Children may know that a key opens a door or lock.
clear, page 111	Explain that to clear the calculator means to erase the numbers that are showing.
mystery bag, page 113	A mystery is something that is unknown. A mystery bag is a bag that contains unknown things that you cannot see.

Building Academic Language: Numeral Variations

The numerals displayed on a calculator may look slightly different from the numerals children write. This is similar to how alphabet letters in printed books look different from the alphabet letters children learn to form. Use a chart to describe and compare the differences between numerals on the calculator and numerals children write.

Checking for Understanding

Use the prompts below, your own questions, and the master on page 110 to plan comprehension checks for English Learners.

English Proficiency	Prompts
Beginning	*Put a label on the calculator.*
Early Intermediate	*What does this label say? Does this label match this object?*
Intermediate	*What are three things in this classroom that do not have labels?*

Providing Access: Using Sentence Frames

Give children additional practice using language to estimate the time. Move the hour hand of the clock to various positions and ask the class to tell about what time it is. Provide sentence frames: *It is about ____ , almost ____ , just before ____ , a little after ____ ,* and *between ____ and ____ .*

Previewing Vocabulary

An explanation of words with multiple meanings, key math terms, and common procedural vocabulary may aid student comprehension. Consider previewing these terms and reinforcing them as they are used in the lesson.

Words and Phrases	Meanings
a minute long, page 115	Anything lasting a minute is a minute long. Note that the word *long* may be confusing to children in this context because it is not used with inches, feet, centimeters, or meters.
hour hand, page 115	On an analog clock, the short pointer that moves most slowly is the hour hand. It points to the hour on the clock and changes position as it gets closer to the next hour.
watch the hour hand, page 116	To look at is to watch. In this phrase, *watch* is an action, different from a watch worn on the wrist.

Building Academic Language: Silent Letter *h*

In English, there are some words that have a silent *h* such as *hour* and *honest.* Point out the silent *h* in *hour* to children. It is an important spelling distinction between the homophones *hour* and *our.* Note that the letter *h* in Spanish is always silent.

Checking for Understanding

Use the prompts below, your own questions, and the master on page 110 to plan comprehension checks for English Learners.

English Proficiency	Prompts
Beginning	*On the demonstration clock, show that it is almost three o'clock. Now, show a little after 5 o'clock.*
Early Intermediate	*Is it almost 3 or almost 4 o'clock? Does "It is almost 2 o'clock" mean the same as "It is about 2 o'clock"?*
Intermediate	*What is another way to say "It is almost 2 o'clock"?*

Telling Time to the Hour

Providing Access: Using Sentence Frames and Templates

Help English Learners build confidence using expressions by providing sentence frames for oral or written language patterns. (This may be especially helpful for the future verb tense, which English Learners may be less familiar with.)

Previewing Vocabulary

An explanation of words with multiple meanings, key math terms, and common procedural vocabulary may aid student comprehension. Consider previewing these terms and reinforcing them as they are used in the lesson.

Words and Phrases	Meanings
clock face, page 121	The flat surface of the clock that has the numbers on it is the face.
midnight, page 121	12 o'clock at night is called *midnight. Mid* means middle so midnight is the middle of the night.
noon, page 121	12 o'clock in the daytime is called *noon,* which is 12 hours after midnight.
telling time, page 121	To look at the clock and say the hour and minutes is to tell time.

Building Academic Language: Future Tense

English Learners in the early levels of proficiency often have opportunities to talk about events in the present and past. However, children may have less experience with discussing events in the future. Often, the future verb tense is used to describe time. Provide sentence frames for children to use: *What time will it be when <u>we leave school</u>? It will be <u>2:30</u>.*

Checking for Understanding

Use the prompts below, your own questions, and the master on page 110 to plan comprehension checks for English Learners.

English Proficiency	Prompts
Beginning	*Show on the demonstration clock what time you wake up in the morning.*
Early Intermediate	*Do we eat lunch at noon or at midnight?*
Intermediate	*Explain what "the water drains in a clockwise direction" means.*

Explorations: Exploring Lengths, Straightedges, and Dominoes

Providing Access: Familiar Customs

The game of dominoes is a popular pastime in many countries. Ask children if they are familiar with dominoes and suggest that children play a game with their families. Then, discuss their strategies for playing successfully.

Previewing Vocabulary

An explanation of words with multiple meanings, key math terms, and common procedural vocabulary may aid student comprehension. Consider previewing these terms and reinforcing them as they are used in the lesson.

Words and Phrases	Meanings
figure out, page 126	To solve a problem or to determine the answer is to figure it out.
dots, page 126	Small round marks are called *dots* and are often brightly colored and arranged in patterns.

Building Academic Language: Nontransferable Skill—Ending Sounds

In this lesson, lengths and the relative lengths of objects are discussed. The word *lengths* has five consonants clustered at the end of the word, making it very difficult for some English Learners to pronounce. If this ending sound does not exist in children's home languages, it will be more difficult for them to perceive and produce in English. Model the pronunciation of *lengths* and other words with clusters of consonants by articulating them carefully.

Checking for Understanding

Use the prompts below, your own questions, and the master on page 110 to plan comprehension checks for English Learners.

English Proficiency	Prompts
Beginning	*With your hands, show the length of your shoe.*
Early Intermediate	*When we talk about how long something is, do we describe its width or length?*
Intermediate	*How could you compare the lengths of two objects?*

Pennies

Providing Access: Exploring Customs

Explain that in the United States, some sporting contests such as professional football games begin with the toss of a coin to determine which team goes first. Each team chooses heads or tails. Every U.S. coin has a portrait on one side of the coin, referred to as *heads*. The other side, referred to as *tails*, has a picture of a place or historical event. Tell children to find the portrait on the penny. Ask: *Who is this?*

Previewing Vocabulary

An explanation of words with multiple meanings, key math terms, and common procedural vocabulary may aid student comprehension. Consider previewing these terms and reinforcing them as they are used in the lesson.

Words and Phrases	Meanings
piggy bank, page 130	A ceramic or plastic container for saving change, originally shaped like a pig, is called a *piggy bank*.
upside down, page 132	Explain that when you turn something that faces up so that it is facing down, it is upside down. Demonstrate with a cup as you explain.
mint date, page 133	Every U.S. coin has a year printed on it that tells when the coin was made. This is the mint date.

Building Academic Language: Hard and Soft Sounds of *c*

Review with children the different sounds *c* can make:

Hard *C* sounds like /k/ when followed by *a*, *o*, or *u*	Soft *C* sounds like /s/ when followed by *e*, *i*, or *y*
can	cent
coin	circle
count	cycle
cut	dice

Checking for Understanding

Use the prompts below, your own questions, and the master on page 110 to plan comprehension checks for English Learners.

English Proficiency	Prompts
Beginning	*Find a penny that was minted in the same year you were born. Find a penny that was minted this year.*
Early Intermediate	*What side of the penny shows the portrait of Abraham Lincoln, heads or tails?*
Intermediate	*What does it mean to mint a coin?*

Providing Access: Connecting to Everyday Life

Working in small groups, children gain practice speaking and benefit from listening to the ideas of others. In this lesson, children learn about nickels. Ask children to show thumbs-up or thumbs-down if they think the following are worth five cents: a book, a cup of lemonade, a pencil, a sticker. Have children brainstorm in small groups three things worth five cents.

Previewing Vocabulary

An explanation of words with multiple meanings, key math terms, and common procedural vocabulary may aid student comprehension. Consider previewing these terms and reinforcing them as they are used in the lesson.

Words and Phrases	Meanings
end up with, page 137	This phrase refers to what you finish the game with or what you have at the end. For example, try to end up with the fewest number of coins.
scratch paper, page 139	Paper that may be used to write calculations on but is not turned in for review is scratch paper. In this expression, *scratch* means that the paper might have cross outs and erasures on it.
pool their pennies, page 139	Explain that when players put all their pennies together in one big, shared amount or pool, they pool their pennies.

Building Academic Language: Initials

Explain that in English the first letter of a word is used to stand for the whole word. Point out that when drawing pennies for this lesson, children write the letter *p* in a circle. This is much quicker than writing out the whole word. Explain how initials are used to stand for a person's first and last names.

Checking for Understanding

Use the prompts below, your own questions, and the master on page 110 to plan comprehension checks for English Learners.

English Proficiency	Prompts
Beginning	*Trade five pennies for one nickel.*
Early Intermediate	*Are five nickels worth one penny? How many pennies are worth one nickel? Which is worth more, six pennies or two nickels?*
Intermediate	*Which is worth more, seven pennies or three nickels? Why?*

Counting Pennies and Nickels

Providing Access: Using Physical Examples

Demonstrate why people use different coin denominations. Have a child hold 100 pennies in one hand and an equal value of nickels in the other. Ask which is easier to carry around. Explain that one reason different coins are used is to make it easier to carry larger amounts of money. Discuss with children that they will be trading for dimes, quarters, and dollar bills.

Previewing Vocabulary

An explanation of words with multiple meanings, key math terms, and common procedural vocabulary may aid student comprehension. Consider previewing these terms and reinforcing them as they are used in the lesson.

Words and Phrases	Meanings
doesn't matter, page 141	Something that doesn't matter does not change the answer and is not important.
die, page 143	One of a pair of dice is a die. Children may try to call it "a dice." They may know *die* as a verb.

Building Academic Language: Plural Nouns

Languages form plurals in different ways. When English Learners transfer their grammar to English, it often results in errors in plural forms. You might hear a child say, "Two boy and three girl." This is because in the primary language, the number word tells the listener that the noun is plural or more than one. Post a plural chart and discuss.

Add -s to the End	Add -es to the End	Words that Change
mark: marks	guess: guesses	die: dice
nickel: nickels	penny: pennies	half: halves

Checking for Understanding

Use the prompts below, your own questions, and the master on page 110 to plan comprehension checks for English Learners.

English Proficiency	Prompts
Beginning	Draw the number of pennies that equal two nickels.
Early Intermediate	Which is worth more, five pennies or five nickels? Which would you rather have?
Intermediate	Which is better to carry in your pocket, 50 cents in pennies or 50 cents in nickels? Why?

Number Models

Providing Access: Using Diagrams

Connect a visual representation to new concepts to aid student comprehension. This strategy enables English Learners to understand lesson content without having to rely solely on language. This is very important in mathematics because many terms have multiple meanings. See page 147 of the *Teacher's Lesson Guide,* for how diagrams can reinforce conceptual understanding and new vocabulary. Children who know the plus and equal signs in their home languages will find that the signs transfer to English.

Previewing Vocabulary

An explanation of words with multiple meanings, key math terms, and common procedural vocabulary may aid student comprehension. Consider previewing these terms and reinforcing them as they are used in the lesson.

Words and Phrases	Meanings
plus sign, page 147	A *sign* is a symbol that represents a meaning that everyone understands. The *plus sign* means to add.
teeth, page 148	More than one tooth are called *teeth*.

Building Academic Language: Double Consonants

In English, many words have double consonants. List the following words from the lesson on a chart: *pennies, tennis ball, class, tell, correct,* and *add*. Children may be able to add others. Circle the double consonants and say the words. In English, double consonants are pronounced as if they were a single letter. In Spanish and some other languages, *rr* and *ll* have different pronunciations than the single *r* and *l*.

Checking for Understanding

Use the prompts below, your own questions, and the master on page 110 to plan comprehension checks for English Learners.

English Proficiency	Prompts
Beginning	*Draw a number model that adds your age to the age of the student next to you.*
Early Intermediate	*The + is called a _____ sign.* *The = is called an _____ sign.*
Intermediate	*What do we call this: 8 + 4 = 12?*

Subtraction Number Models

Providing Access: Procedural Language

In this lesson, children play games which hone their skills and provide a context for language practice. Some children may have experience with board games, card games, or strategy games. Others may not be as familiar with games in English. Introduce basic terminology used in the following phrases: *taking turns, skipping a turn, picking* a card, deciding who *goes* first, and what to do in a *tie*.

Previewing Vocabulary

An explanation of words with multiple meanings, key math terms, and common procedural vocabulary may aid student comprehension. Consider previewing these terms and reinforcing them as they are used in the lesson.

Words and Phrases	Meanings
in a row, page 151	One right after another is *in a row*, which can refer to physical objects like the paper cups in this lesson, or things like three turns in a row.
left standing, page 151	Anything still standing when the action is over is left standing. Children may know the directional word *left* but explain it is used differently here.
check their answers, page 152	To review answers to make sure they are correct is to check them.
answer blank, page 152	A space or line to write the answer on is an answer blank.

Building Academic Language: Practicing Questions

When appropriate, use the Enrichment activities in Part 3 of the lesson with English Learners. In this lesson, explain the question in the game Who am I thinking of? and rehearse it with children. See page 155 in the *Teacher's Lesson Guide.*

Checking for Understanding

Use the prompts below, your own questions, and the master on page 110 to plan comprehension checks for English Learners.

English Proficiency	Prompts
Beginning	*Draw the minus sign on your slate. Does it mean add? Does it mean subtract?*
Early Intermediate	*Draw and label the plus sign, the minus sign, and the equal sign. Show a number model using the minus sign.*
Intermediate	*Write a number model and explain what it means.*

Number Stories

Providing Access: Drawing Symbols as Visual Aids

English Learners at early levels of proficiency may understand the math concepts well but have difficulty communicating their understanding. Encourage English Learners to draw symbols to represent their ideas and use this strategy to solve number stories.

Previewing Vocabulary

An explanation of words with multiple meanings, key math terms, and common procedural vocabulary may aid student comprehension. Consider previewing these terms and reinforcing them as they are used in the lesson.

Words and Phrases	Meanings
makes sense, page 157	Explain that something makes sense when you know what it means.
pile, page 158	A pile is like a stack but is less organized. Think of a pile of clothes in the laundry. A pile is a number of items grouped together.
facedown, page 159	Explain that when you lie down on your stomach, your face is down and people cannot see who you are. When cards are facedown, the numbers are not showing.
stack, page 159	A tall pile or a number of items lying neatly on top of one another is a stack, for example, a stack of books or cards.

Building Academic Language: Using a Graphic Organizer

Have children use a storyboard or a flow chart to sketch a number story they want to solve. Ask children to work with a partner to put words to their story. Explain that the pictures, numbers, and symbols should reinforce the meaning for the reader. Graphic organizers allow the teacher to see the flow of ideas and story line, which can provide a better picture of children's understanding than relying solely on their language production.

Checking for Understanding

Use the prompts below, your own questions, and the master on page 110 to plan comprehension checks for English Learners.

English Proficiency	Prompts
Beginning	*Work with a partner who speaks your home language. Talk about how to act out one of the number stories. Role-play the number story in English.*
Early Intermediate	*Share the number models you made when solving the number stories in your math journal.*
Intermediate	*Explain how to solve the number story using a number model.*

Visual Patterns

Providing Access: Illustrating New Vocabulary

Support comprehension of new vocabulary by having children draw pictures or symbols to represent word meanings. This strategy helps teachers see what children believe the word means and demonstrates experience or prior knowledge children have with the words.

Previewing Vocabulary

An explanation of words with multiple meanings, key math terms, and common procedural vocabulary may aid student comprehension. Consider previewing these terms and reinforcing them as they are used in the lesson.

Words and Phrases	Meanings
craft sticks, page 183	Small, rounded, wooden sticks used for making crafts are craft sticks.
color-code, page 185	To match colors to objects, patterns, or symbols is to color-code. The word *code* means that symbols are used to make something known.
hand, page 185	Explain that in a card game, this is the set of cards that you are holding in your hand and playing at that time.
turn is over, page 185	When your turn is finished (done), it is no longer your turn to play. Your turn is over.

Building Academic Language: Cognates

It may help children to see the connection between their home language and English. Words that end with *-al* share the same roots in English and Spanish. For example, *horizontal* and *vertical* have the same spellings and meanings in both languages. Make a list of other English words that end in *-al,* such as *visual, normal,* and *diagonal.* Encourage children to add words.

Checking for Understanding

Use the prompts below, your own questions, and the master on page 110 to plan comprehension checks for English Learners.

English Proficiency	Prompts
Beginning	*Find a simple pattern in the classroom and point to it. Draw the pattern.*
Early Intermediate	*Do you see any squares in this pattern? What shapes do you see in this pattern?*
Intermediate	*Describe the color and shape of a pattern you see in our classroom.*

Even and Odd Number Patterns

Providing Access: Using Words and Gestures

English Learners of Beginning proficiency may need alternative ways to explain or describe the patterns they work with in this lesson. Encourage children to accompany their descriptions with gestures to help them share their answers. Reinforce words that describe size, direction, and shape with hand gestures and demonstrations.

Previewing Vocabulary

An explanation of words with multiple meanings, key math terms, and common procedural vocabulary may aid student comprehension. Consider previewing these terms and reinforcing them as they are used in the lesson.

Words and Phrases	Meanings
even, page 189	In Spanish, the word for *even* is *par* which means "pair." A pair of objects is even, with no leftovers.
table, page 190	Rows and columns for organizing data (numbers) form a table, which is different from the everyday meaning of a *table* as furniture. See page 72 in *My Reference Book* for examples to show children.
model, page 190	To demonstrate how to do something while explaining how to do it is to model.
land on, page 193	Explain that in a board game when a game piece stops and comes to rest on a spot or place, it lands on that place.

Building Academic Language: Expanding Vocabulary

To reinforce the concept of pairs in this lesson, create a chart of things that come in pairs. Discuss the following with children and ask them to name other items to add to the list: shoes, dice, earrings, and socks.

Checking for Understanding

Use the prompts below, your own questions, and the master on page 110 to plan comprehension checks for English Learners.

English Proficiency	Prompts
Beginning	*Use your counters to show three odd numbers. Now, make them into even numbers.*
Early Intermediate	*Tell whether these are odd or even numbers: 2, 4, 6, 8…*
	Tell whether these are odd or even numbers: 3, 5, 7, 9…
Intermediate	*Use counters to show three odd numbers. How do you know they are odd numbers?*

Providing Access: Using Visual References

As children work with number grids, make a poster of key words like *column, row,* and *diagonal.* Write each word in the direction they describe. (See page 198 of this lesson for an example.)

Previewing Vocabulary

An explanation of words with multiple meanings, key math terms, and common procedural vocabulary may aid student comprehension. Consider previewing these terms and reinforcing them as they are used in the lesson.

Words and Phrases	Meanings
dots, page 195	Small round marks are dots; often they are brightly colored and arranged in patterns.
raincoat, page 196	A waterproof coat to keep rain off your clothes is a raincoat.
shorts, page 196	Pants with the pant legs cut off above the knee are shorts.

Building Academic Language: Cognates

Some languages share words and roots that have similar spellings and meanings. In this lesson, children discuss weather and probability. Many of the English words that end with *-ble* mean the same in Spanish and are spelled similarly. It may help Spanish speakers if you point out these words and add them to a two-column list of English and Spanish words. For example: *impossible/imposible, possible/posible,* and *probable/probable.*

Checking for Understanding

Use the prompts below, your own questions, and the master on page 110 to plan comprehension checks for English Learners.

English Proficiency	Prompts
Beginning	*Do you think it is likely to snow today?*
Early Intermediate	*What kind of weather do you think we will have today?*
Intermediate	*Describe the weather today.*

Explorations: Exploring Number Patterns, Shapes, and Patterns

Providing Access: Using Rhythm and Chant

Using rhythm is an excellent way to help English Learners practice patterns because the rhythms themselves are patterns, and they make it easier to remember and predict the words. As children work with pattern blocks, encourage them to create a rhythm such as, "Square, square, circle, square," or "Rectangle, rectangle, circle, square."

Previewing Vocabulary

An explanation of words with multiple meanings, key math terms, and common procedural vocabulary may aid student comprehension. Consider previewing these terms and reinforcing them as they are used in the lesson.

Words and Phrases	Meanings
sorting, page 200	To separate into different sets according to some shared characteristics or attributes, such as color, size, number, or shape, is called *sorting*.
answer blank, page 201	An empty space often with a blank line for filling in an answer on a test or assignment is an answer blank.

Building Academic Language: Position Words

One element of English that is often difficult for young English Learners is position words. In this lesson, children create designs using slides, flips, and turns. Have children use position words such as *above, below,* and *to the right of* to describe how they create their designs. Make a poster that shows each of these positions and the corresponding words.

Checking for Understanding

Use the prompts below, your own questions, and the master on page 110 to plan comprehension checks for English Learners.

English Proficiency	Prompts
Beginning	*Place three red triangles in a horizontal row. Now, place one blue circle above each triangle...*
Early Intermediate	*Name your pattern using a rhythm to help others learn it.*
Intermediate	*Describe your pattern including the shape, color, and position of each shape in your design.*

Providing Access: Using Physical Movement

Incorporate physical movement to aid comprehension. Create a large number line on the floor that extends below zero. Make sure the 0 is on the right and that the negative numbers extend to the left. Call off a negative number and a movement (hop, tiptoe, skip) and have a child move to the number as indicated. Assess children's understanding and correct any misunderstandings.

Previewing Vocabulary

An explanation of words with multiple meanings, key math terms, and common procedural vocabulary may aid student comprehension. Consider previewing these terms and reinforcing them as they are used in the lesson.

Words and Phrases	Meanings
below zero, page 205	Negative numbers are those below zero on the number line. A temperature of 0°C is freezing, so temperatures below zero are extremely cold.
slanted, page 205	A diagonal line is a slanted line. Slanted lines are straight lines that are not vertical or horizontal.
negative number line, page 208	A negative number line shows numbers that come before zero.

Building Academic Language: Cognates

Some languages share words and roots. These shared spellings and meanings may help English Learners acquire new words quickly. In this lesson, children work with positive and negative numbers. Make a list of words that end with -ive in English and -ivo in Spanish, such as *positive/positivo, negative/negativo,* and *active/activo.*

Checking for Understanding

Use the prompts below, your own questions, and the master on page 110 to plan comprehension checks for English Learners.

English Proficiency	Prompts
Beginning	*Use the floor number line to show the direction of negative numbers. Walk to −3. Now go count back 3 more. What number are you on?*
Early Intermediate	*Is 0 a negative number or a positive number?*
Intermediate	*Is 0 a negative number or a positive number? Explain.*

Adding and Subtracting on the Number Line

Providing Access: The Student as Teacher

English Learners may benefit from giving commands and asking questions in the context of the lesson content. Have children work with a partner of a different English proficiency level to create three problems for others in the class to solve using the floor number line. Place several model questions on the board for reference.

Previewing Vocabulary

An explanation of words with multiple meanings, key math terms, and common procedural vocabulary may aid student comprehension. Consider previewing these terms and reinforcing them as they are used in the lesson.

Words and Phrases	Meanings
model cars, page 210	A small plastic or metal car that looks like a real car is a model car.
dozen, page 211	Twelve of one kind of an item is called a *dozen*. Eggs come in a dozen.
match, page 213	Explain that to match numbers, words, or objects, you pair up two items that share characteristics or that mean the same thing.

Building Academic Language: Irregular Past Tense

Number stories are often told in the past tense. English Learners may find this confusing, especially when some of the verbs are irregular past tense, that is, they are formed by changing the base word instead of adding -*ed* to the end. Underline or write on the board verbs from each number story to discuss. *Cynthia <u>had</u> 8 model cars. She <u>got</u> 3 more. Five eggs <u>broke</u>. How many eggs <u>did not break</u>?* (See the number stories on pages 210 and 211 of this lesson.)

Checking for Understanding

Use the prompts below, your own questions, and the master on page 110 to plan comprehension checks for English Learners.

English Proficiency	Prompts
Beginning	*Listen to the number story and show on the number line how to solve the problem.*
Early Intermediate	*Listen to the number models and write them down. Don't forget to use the +, −, and = symbols in your number model.*
Intermediate	*Make up a number story for 2 + 2 = 4 and tell it to a partner.*

Telling Time to the Half-Hour

Providing Access: Cultural Notes about Time

Time is a construct that differs from culture to culture and language to language. In most places in the United States, there is a strong expectation that big events such as a wedding or a graduation will begin on time and that arriving on time is a sign of respect and interest. As students study time, share cultural expectations, such as this, with them and their families.

Previewing Vocabulary

An explanation of words with multiple meanings, key math terms, and common procedural vocabulary may aid student comprehension. Consider previewing these terms and reinforcing them as they are used in the lesson.

Words and Phrases	Meanings
set the clock, page 218	Explain that to adjust the time on the clock, you set the clock. People set clocks after the power goes out.
tell time, page 218	To look at the clock and say the hour and minutes is to tell time.
half-past, page 218	Explain that when it is thirty minutes after the hour, it is called *half-past the hour*. The minute hand has gone halfway around the clock.

Building Academic Language: Compound Words

Help English Learners understand words by dividing them into parts. In this lesson, *halfway* is discussed, for example, "the minute hand is halfway around the clock." Explain that *halfway* is made up of two small words. These words keep their meaning. Demonstrate how to determine the meaning of other compound words, such as *half-past* and *tool-kit,* as children encounter them in the lesson.

Checking for Understanding

Use the prompts below, your own questions, and the master on page 110 to plan comprehension checks for English Learners.

English Proficiency	Prompts
Beginning	*Show three-thirty on your clock. Now show half-past three. Are these times the same?*
Early Intermediate	*What time is this?*
Intermediate	*What is the difference between three o'clock and three-thirty?*

Introduction to the Frames-and-Arrows Routine

Providing Access: Using Diagrams to Solve Problems

Challenge critical thinking without heavily increasing the linguistic demand on English Learners by using graphic organizers, such as the Frames-and-Arrows diagrams. It may be helpful for children of Beginning English proficiency to work with a partner.

Previewing Vocabulary

An explanation of words with multiple meanings, key math terms, and common procedural vocabulary may aid student comprehension. Consider previewing these terms and reinforcing them as they are used in the lesson.

Words and Phrases	Meanings
picture frame, page 220	A wood or plastic outline for a photograph or picture to protect it and help show off the picture is a picture frame.
empty frame, page 221	A frame with nothing inside is empty. Tell children Frames-and-Arrows diagrams contain empty frames for them to fill in their answers.
missing number, page 221	An unknown number is a missing number. Tell children that they have to find the missing number in Frames and Arrows.

Building Academic Language: Nontransferable Skill—Silent *e*

Not all languages have silent letters but English has several. Start a word list of key vocabulary terms in this unit that have a silent final letter *e*. Ask children what each of these words has in common: *rule, dime, solve*.

Checking for Understanding

Use the prompts below, your own questions, and the master on page 110 to plan comprehension checks for English Learners.

English Proficiency	Prompts
Beginning	*Show on the number line how to count up by 2s.*
Early Intermediate	*Name the rule in this Frames-and-Arrows problem.*
Intermediate	*What is the rule? How do you know?*

More Frames-and-Arrows Problems

Providing Access: Using Chants and Rhymes

Using chants, rhymes, and rhythms are very effective ways of helping English Learners learn new material. In this lesson, children look for the arrow rule using a Frames-and-Arrows diagram. Help them by reciting a new version of a cheer they learned: *1, 3, 5, 7, 9. First graders are mighty fine.* This is similar to *2, 4, 6, 8. First graders are really great.*

Previewing Vocabulary

An explanation of words with multiple meanings, key math terms, and common procedural vocabulary may aid student comprehension. Consider previewing these terms and reinforcing them as they are used in the lesson.

Words and Phrases	Meanings
mystery problem, page 225	A mystery is something that is unknown. A mystery problem is a problem that children have to solve, for example, finding the rule in a Frames-and-Arrows problem.
figure out, page 225	To solve a problem or to find the answer is to figure it out.
make up your own, page 226	To create or invent something on your own is to make it up. Here, *make up* is an action and the phrase is a direction for children to make up their own problems.

Building Academic Language: Collocations

Many English Learners understand the word *count* but in English the word *count* changes meanings when it is part of a set phrase, called a *collocation*. Have groups list phrases with the word *count* in them; for example, *skip count, count up, count back,* and *count by.* Have children create simple books of these phrases and illustrate the mathematical meaning of each.

Checking for Understanding

Use the prompts below, your own questions, and the master on page 110 to plan comprehension checks for English Learners.

English Proficiency	Prompts
Beginning	*Work with a partner to solve the Frames-and-Arrows problems. Use the number line to help with the more difficult problems.*
Early Intermediate	*Select one of the patterns in the Frames-and-Arrows problems and read it aloud.*
Intermediate	*Select one of the patterns in the Frames-and-Arrows problem and read it aloud. Describe the counting pattern.*

Providing Access: Using Math Tools

In this lesson, children learn to use the calculator to count. Math tools not only help children count, but are interesting to them. Because children are motivated to use calculators, they gain additional practice. English Learners benefit from the support and extra counting practice that the calculator offers.

Previewing Vocabulary

An explanation of words with multiple meanings, key math terms, and common procedural vocabulary may aid student comprehension. Consider previewing these terms and reinforcing them as they are used in the lesson.

Words and Phrases	Meanings
key, page 230	The buttons on the calculator are keys and in this context are not the keys to unlock doors.
program, page 231	(v.) To instruct a calculator to repeat a calculation using its memory instead of having the user enter a key sequence over and over is to program it.
display, page 232	(n.) The window on the calculator where you can see the numbers is the display.

Building Academic Language: Words with Multiple Meanings

Some math tools such as computers, rulers, scales, and calculators have special vocabulary. Have English Learners draw an enlarged picture of a calculator and add descriptive labels. Discuss some of the following terminology that have other meanings in everyday usage: *key, display* (used here as a noun), *clear* the calculator, and *program* (as a verb).

Checking for Understanding

Use the prompts below, your own questions, and the master on page 110 to plan comprehension checks for English Learners.

English Proficiency	Prompts
Beginning	*Show how to program the calculator to count by 2s.*
Early Intermediate	*When you tell the calculator to repeat a calculation using its memory, you _____ the calculator.*
Intermediate	*Explain step by step how to program the calculator to count by 2s.*

Dimes

Providing Access: Addressing Misconceptions

At this age, children often equate more coins with more value. They may also think that the size of the coin helps to determine the value. Have children create a chart of values by tracing around each coin and showing how many coins equal another coin. Children may enjoy listening to the poem "Proud" by Shel Silverstein that tells how a young boy received a dollar bill from his father and traded it for a few cents because two is more than one.

Previewing Vocabulary

An explanation of words with multiple meanings, key math terms, and common procedural vocabulary may aid student comprehension. Consider previewing these terms and reinforcing them as they are used in the lesson.

Words and Phrases	Meanings
exchange, page 238	To trade is to exchange. When you give something to another person and they give you something in return, you make an exchange. Here, children exchange coins.
high five, page 239	To slap the palm of your friend's hand with your hand high in the air is a high five. Demonstrate for children.
harder coin combinations, page 239	Harder combinations are more difficult. Explain this use of *hard* is different from a hard surface.

Building Academic Language: Nontransferable Skill—Final /th/

Explain that when talking about money, people often ask about value, what something is *worth*. This word, and others that end with *-th*, may be difficult for some English Learners to pronounce because the /th/ sound is not used in their home language in the final position. Ask children to add English words that end with *-th* to a list. Model pronunciation by articulating words carefully.

Checking for Understanding

Use the prompts below, your own questions, and the master on page 110 to plan comprehension checks for English Learners.

English Proficiency	Prompts
Beginning	*Show on your hands, how much a dime is worth.*
Early Intermediate	*How many children are in our class? How many dimes would our class have if everyone had one?*
Intermediate	*Follow this "if... then" model to complete the statement: If every child in our class had one dime, then our class would have _____.*

Counting Dimes, Nickels, and Pennies

Providing Access: Using Real Objects

Using real objects or replicas helps make new concepts more concrete. Throughout this lesson, English Learners use real coins or coins in their tool kits to practice working with values. Invite children to bring in coins from other countries to share.

Previewing Vocabulary

An explanation of words with multiple meanings, key math terms, and common procedural vocabulary may aid student comprehension. Consider previewing these terms and reinforcing them as they are used in the lesson.

Words and Phrases	Meanings
coin, page 244	A small round piece of metal stamped with a design and used as money is a coin.
value, page 245	What something is worth is its value.

Building Academic Language: *How Much* and *How Many*

Point out the difference between questions that begin with *how much* and *how many*. The question "How much money do you have?" is asking for a total value. The question "How many coins and bills do you have?" is asking for a specific number of coins or bills. Ask children: *How many dimes do you have?*

Checking for Understanding

Use the prompts below, your own questions, and the master on page 110 to plan comprehension checks for English Learners.

English Proficiency	Prompts
Beginning	Hold up a nickel. *Is this a nickel? Draw five pennies on your paper.* Hold up a penny. *Is this a penny?*
Early Intermediate	*How many pennies do you have? How many nickels do you have?* Show four nickels in your hand. *Are these pennies or nickels?*
Intermediate	*What is the value of 2 nickels and 2 pennies? How do you know?*

Lesson 3·13 Data Day

Providing Access: Using Graphic Organizers

When working with English Learners, teachers face the challenge of making the lesson rigorous and comprehensible. Graphic organizers promote higher-level thinking by helping children to show, compare, contrast, or organize data without requiring lots of language. In this lesson, children participate in making a line plot by beginning with a tally chart. English Learners understand the construction of the line plot more clearly when they see step by step how the data is collected and demonstrated.

Previewing Vocabulary

An explanation of words with multiple meanings, key math terms, and common procedural vocabulary may aid student comprehension. Consider previewing these terms and reinforcing them as they are used in the lesson.

Words and Phrases	Meanings
siblings, page 247	Brothers and sisters are siblings.
survey, page 247	Questions for gathering information from a large group of people are in a survey. Surveys usually ask "yes" or "no" questions or multiple-choice questions.
coins that are left, page 248	Children may know the word *left* as a direction word. Here it describes the coins that remain or are extra.

Building Academic Language: *Which* and *What*

When forming questions about the data tally in this lesson, help children use the words *which* and *what* correctly. A question starting with *which* asks about a choice of things. For example, "Which column has the most stick-on notes?" A question beginning with *what* is used to find out more about something or someone. For example, "What does this chart show?"

Checking for Understanding

Use the prompts below, your own questions, and the master on page 110 to plan comprehension checks for English Learners.

English Proficiency	Prompts
Beginning	*Which column shows how many siblings you have? Point to the column that shows one less sibling than in your family.*
Early Intermediate	*What are siblings?*
Intermediate	*Explain how to conduct a survey.*

Domino Addition

Providing Access: Creating a Math Word Bank

Throughout *Everyday Mathematics*, English Learners are encouraged to make and add to a Math Word Bank. A template is provided on page 109 of this handbook. Children write the new words, draw pictures to represent them, and write other words that describe them. English Learners may find it helpful to record some of the related words in their home language.

Previewing Vocabulary

An explanation of words with multiple meanings, key math terms, and common procedural vocabulary may aid student comprehension. Consider previewing these terms and reinforcing them as they are used in the lesson.

Words and Phrases	Meanings
blank, page 252	The side of the domino with no dots is blank.
cutout dominoes, page 253	A *cutout* is a shape made of paper with a pattern printed on it so that it can be cut out of paper or from a book.
clenched fist, page 254	Explain that when you fold in your fingers, you form a fist. A clenched fist is a fist that is tightly folded.

Building Academic Language: Cognates

In this lesson, children work with visual patterns on dominoes. They count the total number of dots. English Learners who speak Spanish may also know the word *total* because it is spelled the same and means the same in Spanish. Look for other multisyllabic English words that end with *-al,* such as *horizontal, vertical, visual,* and *diagonal,* to point out to children because they are the same in Spanish. Collect *-al* words from this unit in a word list. Remember, single syllable words like *pal* do not fit this cognate pattern.

Checking for Understanding

Use the prompts below, your own questions, and the master on page 110 to plan comprehension checks for English Learners.

English Proficiency	Prompts
Beginning	*Sort the dominoes. Put all the dominoes with an odd number of dots in one pile.*
Early Intermediate	*Are these dominoes odd or even? Show how you know. Do "sum" and "total" mean the same thing?*
Intermediate	*Explain how you know this domino has an odd number of dots.*

Math Message and Reading a Thermometer

Providing Access: Using Rebuses

When writing on the board, using rebuses or symbols can be a helpful way to explain concepts to English Learners. A *rebus* is a small picture that takes the place of a written word. Using rebuses makes more advanced material accessible to children at beginning English proficiency levels. Use rebuses or pictures as you write Math Messages.

Previewing Vocabulary

An explanation of words with multiple meanings, key math terms, and common procedural vocabulary may aid student comprehension. Consider previewing these terms and reinforcing them as they are used in the lesson.

Words and Phrases	Meanings
thumbs-up, page 276	Thumbs-up is a positive signal used to show agreement.
fists, page 276	A fist is formed by folding in your fingers.
facedown, page 278	Explain that when you lie on your stomach, your face is down and people cannot tell who you are. When cards are facedown, the numbers are not showing.
a tie, page 278	When runners finish a race with exactly the same time or when teams or people finish a game with the same score, it is called a *tie*.

Building Academic Language: Compound Words

When reading new, unfamiliar words, English Learners may find it helpful to take the word apart to see if they know the meaning of the word parts. Compound words are made up of two or more smaller words that keep their meaning. For example, *classroom* consists of *class* and *room*. Discuss other compound words with children, such as *facedown* and *halfway*. Not all words that have smaller words are compound. For example, *yesterday* is not compound.

Checking for Understanding

Use the prompts below, your own questions, and the master on page 110 to plan comprehension checks for English Learners.

English Proficiency	Prompts
Beginning	*Draw the symbol for degrees. Point to 70°F on the thermometer.*
Early Intermediate	*Which is cooler, 70°F or 75°F? Which is cooler, 70°F or 70°C?*
Intermediate	*What does the °F at the top of the thermometer mean?*

Nonstandard Linear Measures

Providing Access: Expanding Vocabulary

Many English Learners know the words for basic body parts in English. In this lesson, the discussion includes the following phrases that children may need explained: *hand spans, forearms*, and *arm spans*. Have children add labels to the pictures on journal page 56 that depict these phrases.

Previewing Vocabulary

An explanation of words with multiple meanings, key math terms, and common procedural vocabulary may aid student comprehension. Consider previewing these terms and reinforcing them as they are used in the lesson.

Words and Phrases	Meanings
length, page 282	The measure of how long something is, from one end to the other, is its length.
nonstandard, page 283	The opposite of standard is not standard. Nonstandard measuring tools are less exact. A nonstandard measuring tool is a hand. People's hands are different sizes.

Building Academic Language: Comparatives and Superlatives

As children compare individual heights to objects in the room, they may need help with the descriptors. Review this pattern, draw a simple chart, and ask children to add to it. Tell English Learners to ask "how tall," not "how long" children are when measuring.

Positives	Comparatives	Superlatives
long	longer	longest
short	shorter	shortest
tall	taller	tallest

Checking for Understanding

Use the prompts below, your own questions, and the master on page 110 to plan comprehension checks for English Learners.

English Proficiency	Prompts
Beginning	*Is the red bookshelf shorter than the blue bookshelf?*
Early Intermediate	*Which is taller, _____ the red bookshelf, or _____ the blue bookshelf?*
Intermediate	*How much taller is the blue bookshelf than the red bookshelf?*

Personal "Foot" and Standard Foot

Providing Access: Using Sentence Frames

Provide English Learners with model sentences and questions they can practice while learning new concepts. In this lesson, children work with language related to approximation. On a chart or on the board, provide some basic response frames that English Learners can complete and restate: *It measures about ____ feet, a little less than ____ feet,* or *about halfway between ____ and ____.*

Previewing Vocabulary

An explanation of words with multiple meanings, key math terms, and common procedural vocabulary may aid student comprehension. Consider previewing these terms and reinforcing them as they are used in the lesson.

Words and Phrases	Meanings
heel to toe, page 287	This phrase means to put one foot in front of the other foot so the heel of one foot touches the toes of the other.
cutouts, page 288	A *cutout* is a shape made of paper with a pattern printed on it so that it can be cut out of the paper or from a book.

Building Academic Language: Plurals

Not all languages form plurals in the same way. English Learners might transfer their grammar to English resulting in errors in plural forms. You might hear a student say "four cat" or "five dog," because in some languages, the number name tells the listener that the noun is plural or more than one. Post a plural chart and discuss.

Add -s to the End	Add -es to the End	Words that Change
unit: units	inch: inches	foot: feet
		half: halves

Checking for Understanding

Use the prompts below, your own questions, and the master on page 110 to plan comprehension checks for English Learners.

English Proficiency	Prompts
Beginning	*Measure heel to toe from your desk to the front of the classroom.*
Early Intermediate	*Which is longer, the cutout foot or the cutout hand?*
Intermediate	*Would you use your foot or your hand to measure a room? Why?*

The Inch

Providing Access: Using Physical Models

Using authentic measuring tools to measure real objects gives English Learners a deeper conceptual understanding of the units of measure. In this lesson, children measure familiar objects with a ruler. This helps children gain a good idea of approximately how big an inch is.

Previewing Vocabulary

An explanation of words with multiple meanings, key math terms, and common procedural vocabulary may aid student comprehension. Consider previewing these terms and reinforcing them as they are used in the lesson.

Words and Phrases	Meanings
leftover, page 292	Leftovers are what are remaining, extra. What is not used is a leftover.
align, page 293	To line up things in straight lines so that they fit together is to align.
ruler, page 293	A ruler is a measuring tool. Children know the word *rule*, but explain that you do not rule with a ruler, you measure.
telling time, page 295	To look at a clock and say the hour and minutes is telling time.

Building Academic Language: Abbreviations

In this lesson, children learn that *in.* is the abbreviation for *inch*. Explain that in English, abbreviations stand for a longer word. For example, *Mr.* stands for *mister* and *CA* stands for *California*. Have children work with a partner to find abbreviations in the classroom. Make a list of these abbreviations and review their meanings.

Checking for Understanding

Use the prompts below, your own questions, and the master on page 110 to plan comprehension checks for English Learners.

English Proficiency	Prompts
Beginning	*Measure a book using your ruler. How many inches does it measure?*
Early Intermediate	*How long is your hand? How many inches? What else can you find that is the same length as your hand?*
Intermediate	*When is the cutout foot a better tool for measuring than the ruler?*

Providing Access: Using Sentence Frames

Provide English Learners with model sentences and questions they can practice to learn new concepts. In this lesson, children work with the language of measurement. On a chart or on the board, provide basic response frames for English Learners to complete and restate. For example, ask: *About how many blocks long is this object?* Give the following sentence frame: *The ____ is between ____ and ____ blocks long.*

Previewing Vocabulary

An explanation of words with multiple meanings, key math terms, and common procedural vocabulary may aid student comprehension. Consider previewing these terms and reinforcing them as they are used in the lesson.

Words and Phrases	Meanings
estimate, page 299	(v.) To find an answer that is close but not exact is to estimate. Pronounce the third syllable with a long *a* sound, as in *late.*
estimate, page 299	(n.) A guess based on facts is an estimate. Pronounce the third syllable with a schwa sound. For example, *a* in *alone* makes the schwa sound.
reference object, page 299	Explain that an object with a fixed measurement used to refer to when you do not have a ruler and need to measure something is a reference object.

Building Academic Language: Nontransferable Skill—Final /ch/

The word *inch* ends with the /ch/ sound. The sound of /ch/ is a phoneme in English and in Spanish but it does not occur in Spanish at the end of words. English Learners who speak Spanish may add a vowel sound to the end of words that end with -*ch*. Model the /ch/ sound in *inch* by articulating it carefully and give children pronunciation practice.

Checking for Understanding

Use the prompts below, your own questions, and the master on page 110 to plan comprehension checks for English Learners.

English Proficiency	Prompts
Beginning	*Show me something that measures about 3 inches.*
Early Intermediate	*Name three objects that are longer than your foot.*
Intermediate	*Explain how to measure something that is longer than the 6-inch ruler.*

Measuring with a Tape Measure

Providing Access: Expanding Vocabulary

Many English Learners know the words for the basic body parts in English, but in this lesson, the discussion includes the following words that may be new: *wrist, ankle, elbow*, and *hand spans*. Add a label to the corresponding pictures on journal page 66.

Previewing Vocabulary

An explanation of words with multiple meanings, key math terms, and common procedural vocabulary may aid student comprehension. Consider previewing these terms and reinforcing them as they are used in the lesson.

Words and Phrases	Meanings
flat, page 304	A surface that is smooth and even is flat. The top of a desk is flat.
wrap, page 304	To wrap is to put the tape measure around an object that is not flat to measure how big it is.
overlap, page 304	To cover part of something is to overlap. Demonstrate overlap by placing the fingers of one hand slightly over part of your other hand.

Building Academic Language: Prefixes

In this lesson, children explore the advantages and disadvantages of using a tape measure. Explain that while these words sound similar, they mean the opposite. In English, the prefix *dis-* is added to the word *advantage* to mean that it is not an advantage. Ask children: *What do you think "dis-" means?* Discuss other words that have *dis-* as a prefix, such as *disappear* and *dislike*.

Checking for Understanding

Use the prompts below, your own questions, and the master on page 110 to plan comprehension checks for English Learners.

English Proficiency	Prompts
Beginning	*Can a ruler measure something that is round? Can a tape measure?*
Early Intermediate	*Which is better to measure your waist, a tape measure or a ruler?*
Intermediate	*What is the advantage of using a tape measure?*

Explorations: Exploring Data, Shapes, and Base-10 Blocks

Providing Access: Using Home Language

Use small groups with English Learners so that they can review concepts in their home language. When children are at a very early proficiency level, they may miss important foundational concepts because of limited understanding of English. Encourage children to discuss a topic with others who speak the same primary language to clarify and deepen their understanding.

Previewing Vocabulary

An explanation of words with multiple meanings, key math terms, and common procedural vocabulary may aid student comprehension. Consider previewing these terms and reinforcing them as they are used in the lesson.

Words and Phrases	Meanings
height, page 308	*Height* describes how tall a person is. Reiterate that people do not ask how *high* others are, but rather how *tall* they are.
typical first grader, page 308	*Typical* means common or usual. A typical first grader is like most first graders.
predict, page 310	To guess what will occur based on what is known is to predict.

Building Academic Language: The Sound of *Shapes*

The word *shape* begins with /sh/. The two letters together form a new sound. The sound of /sh/ is not a phoneme in Spanish but is in English. In a minimal pair, it differentiates between two words, for example, *ship* and *chip*. English Learners who speak Spanish may pronounce words that begin with *sh-* using a /ch/ sound, which does exist in Spanish. Model the /sh/ sound in *shape* by articulating it carefully and give children pronunciation practice.

Checking for Understanding

Use the prompts below, your own questions, and the master on page 110 to plan comprehension checks for English Learners.

English Proficiency	Prompts
Beginning	*Who is the tallest person in your class? What is their height?*
Early Intermediate	*Who is taller, you or the teacher? _____ is the tallest person.*
Intermediate	*Explain why you stand next to a wall so a person can measure your height.*

Telling Time on the Quarter-Hour

Providing Access: Many Ways to Say the Same Thing

In this lesson, children build on their time-telling skills. There are a number of ways to tell what time it is. Help children recognize these ways. Make a poster of different ways to describe the quarter-hour. Illustrate and label *quarter-before, quarter-to, quarter-till, quarter-after,* and *quarter-past.*

Previewing Vocabulary

An explanation of words with multiple meanings, key math terms, and common procedural vocabulary may aid student comprehension. Consider previewing these terms and reinforcing them as they are used in the lesson.

Words and Phrases	Meanings
clock face, page 314	The flat surface of the clock that has the numbers on it is the face.
minute hand, page 315	The long pointer on the clock that takes one minute to move from a minute mark to the next minute mark is the minute hand. It moves completely around the clock in one hour.
halfway, page 315	In the middle between two points, or places, is halfway.

Building Academic Language: Words with *qu-*

In this unit, children learn about quarter-hours. The word *quarter* begins with a sound that may not exist in a child's home language. Note that it can be very difficult to pronounce new sounds. For some English Learners, *q* may also be an unfamiliar alphabet letter. For speakers of Spanish, the /kw/ sound exists but is spelled *cua-* as in *cuarto.* Practice pronunciation by having children repeat phrases and other sentences with *qu-: The queen requested a quarter and asked this question, "How many minutes does a quarter-hour equal?"*

Checking for Understanding

Use the prompts below, your own questions, and the master on page 110 to plan comprehension checks for English Learners.

English Proficiency	Prompts
Beginning	*Show on the clock a quarter-to 3. Now show a quarter-past 5.*
Early Intermediate	*How many minutes are in a half-hour? How many minutes are in a quarter-hour?*
Intermediate	*What is the difference between half-past two and two-thirty?*

Providing Access: Using Graphic Organizers

Teachers face the challenge of making a lesson rigorous and comprehensible to English Learners. Graphic organizers promote higher-level thinking by enabling children to show comparisons and contrasts and organize data without requiring lots of language. In this lesson, children make a timeline. This graphic organizer helps English Learners represent the sequence of events and relative lengths of time without having to rely heavily on language.

Previewing Vocabulary

An explanation of words with multiple meanings, key math terms, and common procedural vocabulary may aid student comprehension. Consider previewing these terms and reinforcing them as they are used in the lesson.

Words and Phrases	Meanings
keep track of, page 320	To keep track of something is to make a record of it. People keep track of things they need to do, like go to the dentist.
getting up for school, page 321	This phrase refers to waking up and getting out of bed to get dressed and ready for school in the morning.
end of the month, page 321	The last day of the month is the end of the month.

Building Academic Language: Compound Words

English Learners may find it helpful to take compound words apart to see if they know the meaning of the separate words. Compound words are made up of two or more smaller words that keep their meaning. For example, *wristwatch* is made up of *wrist* and *watch*. Collect and discuss other compound words such as *timeline*, *tick-tock*, and *storybook*. Be careful of words like ***yes**ter**day***. Not all words that are made of smaller words are compound.

Checking for Understanding

Use the prompts below, your own questions, and the master on page 110 to plan comprehension checks for English Learners.

English Proficiency	Prompts
Beginning	*Make a pyramid showing time words with the smallest period of time on top. Include hour, day, minute, year, week, and month.*
Early Intermediate	*Make a list of everything you do in the morning before you come to school. Ask someone for help if you are not sure of a word.*
Intermediate	*How can a timeline be helpful when studying?*

Number Scrolls

Providing Access: Playing Games

Throughout *Everyday Mathematics,* children practice through games. In this lesson, children play *Time Match with Quarter-Hours,* which is an extension of a game they learned previously. Games provide language practice for English Learners as they interact with a partner or small group and engage them in helpful repetition of the language and concept.

Previewing Vocabulary

An explanation of words with multiple meanings, key math terms, and common procedural vocabulary may aid student comprehension. Consider previewing these terms and reinforcing them as they are used in the lesson.

Words and Phrases	Meanings
shortcut, page 326	A quick way of doing something that lessens the amount of time or work you have to do is a shortcut.
just before, page 329	This phrase means immediately before.
check each other's work, page 329	To review another person's work to look for mistakes is to check it.

Building Academic Language: Nontransferable Skill—Consonant Clusters

The word *scroll* begins with the consonant cluster *scr-,* which is not used in many other languages. English Learners may find this sound difficult to pronounce and may try to approximate its pronunciation by adding a vowel syllable in front of *scroll,* or other English words that begin with unfamiliar consonant clusters. Articulate the pronunciation carefully and give children practice pronouncing *scroll* and other words with *scr-.*

Checking for Understanding

Use the prompts below, your own questions, and the master on page 110 to plan comprehension checks for English Learners.

English Proficiency	Prompts
Beginning	*Find the number 200 on your scroll.*
Early Intermediate	*Point to a pattern on your number grid. What are the numbers that make up the pattern?*
Intermediate	*How can you use a number scroll to help you?*

Introducing Fact Power

Providing Access: Playing Games

Create sets of cards for reviewing addition facts. Write the addition facts on one set of cards. On the other set, write the word name for the sum of each fact. Have children play Concentration with sums. When they match the word name of the sum with the corresponding number fact, they get to keep the pair. Punch a hole in each pair that a child matches and place them on a metal or plastic ring for the child to keep.

Previewing Vocabulary

An explanation of words with multiple meanings, key math terms, and common procedural vocabulary may aid student comprehension. Consider previewing these terms and reinforcing them as they are used in the lesson.

Words and Phrases	Meanings
blank domino, page 331	The side of the domino with no dots on it is blank.
shortcut, page 331	A quick way of doing something that lessens the amount of time or work you have to do is a shortcut.
addition facts, page 331	Addition facts are number models that add up two 1-digit numbers to get a sum. Explain that knowing these facts helps you solve other addition problems.

Building Academic Language: Homophones *Sum* and *Some*

When learning a new language, children listen carefully to words and phrases to try to make meaning. In English, some words are *homophones*. That means that the words sound alike but are spelled and defined differently. When children work with addition facts, they learn that addition facts are all *sums* of two 1-digit numbers. Clarify the meanings of the homophones *sum* and *some*.

Checking for Understanding

Use the prompts below, your own questions, and the master on page 110 to plan comprehension checks for English Learners.

English Proficiency	Prompts
Beginning	*Play a game of Sums Concentration with the math fact flashcards. Turn two cards faceup. If the sums match, you keep the pair.*
Early Intermediate	*Recite three addition facts that add up to five.*
Intermediate	*What is fact power?*

Lesson 4·12 Good Fact Habits

Providing Access: Choral Response

Reciting a poem or choral reading can help children memorize new material. The rhythm of the language reinforces the words and makes it easier to remember. Make a large chart with the addition facts for 0, 1, 2, and doubles. Recite the facts aloud: *0 + 0 = 0, 0 + 1 = 1, 0 + 2 = 2* and so on.

Previewing Vocabulary

An explanation of words with multiple meanings, key math terms, and common procedural vocabulary may aid student comprehension. Consider previewing these terms and reinforcing them as they are used in the lesson.

Words and Phrases	Meanings
die, page 337	One of a pair of dice is a die.
tie, page 337	When a race or game ends and both players have the same score, it is called a *tie game* or a *tie score*.
round, page 337	Rounds in a game are periods, episodes, or turns back and forth between players.
highest sum, page 337	The highest sum is the largest sum, the biggest total.

Building Academic Language: Word Family *-ie*

Help English Learners pronounce new words by pointing out word families. Word families are spellings of words that sound alike. For example, *die, tie, pie,* and *lie* are part of the *-ie* word family. Ask children to find other single syllable words that end with *-ie* and make a list.

Checking for Understanding

Use the prompts below, your own questions, and the master on page 110 to plan comprehension checks for English Learners.

English Proficiency	Prompts
Beginning	*What is the sum of 3 + 2?*
Early Intermediate	*Select one addition fact. Say the fact and give the sum.*
Intermediate	*Explain the meaning of a "tie game." How do you break a tie?*

Lesson 5·1

Place Value: Tens and Ones

Providing Access: Modeling

Reinforce the concept of place value by having children demonstrate their understanding of trading and regrouping with physical models. Modeling deepens understanding for English Learners because they do not have to rely solely on language for meaning.

Previewing Vocabulary

An explanation of words with multiple meanings, key math terms, and common procedural vocabulary may aid student comprehension. Consider previewing these terms and reinforcing them as they are used in the lesson.

Words and Phrases	Meanings
right away, page 360	*Right away* means immediately.
deck, page 361	A set of playing cards that go together is a deck of cards.
game is over, page 361	Children may know the word *over* as a position word. This phrase means that the game has finished, ended, or is complete.
shuffle, page 361	To mix up the playing cards in a random manner is to shuffle them.

Building Academic Language: Riddles

In this lesson, children create riddles by using base-10 blocks to give number clues and then ask the question, "Who am I?" Explain that riddles are word games that give several clues to help the listener guess the answer or solve the mystery. Create a template for English Learners to use. *Clue #1: I have _____ tens. Clue #2: I have _____ ones. Who am I?*

Checking for Understanding

Use the prompts below, your own questions, and the master on page 110 to plan comprehension checks for English Learners.

English Proficiency	Prompts
Beginning	*Show the number 41 on your Tens-and-Ones Mat. Show your age on your mat.*
Early Intermediate	*I have 2 tens and 3 ones. What number am I?*
Intermediate	*Add 35 and 35. Explain the trade that is needed.*

Copyright © Wright Group/McGraw-Hill

Place Value with Calculators

Providing Access: Using Math Tools
Some math tools, such as computers, rulers, scales, and calculators have specific vocabulary for using them. Have English Learners draw an enlarged picture of a calculator and add descriptive labels. Discuss some of the terminology that have other meanings in everyday usage, such as *key*, the *display* (used here as a noun), *clear* the calculator, and *program* (as a verb).

Previewing Vocabulary
An explanation of words with multiple meanings, key math terms, and common procedural vocabulary may aid student comprehension. Consider previewing these terms and reinforcing them as they are used in the lesson.

Words and Phrases	Meanings
stands for, page 364	In this context, *stands for* means represents, symbolizes. Tell children that it has nothing to do with physically standing.
two-fisted, page 366	Explain that when you fold in your fingers, you form a fist. *Two-fisted* means to form fists with both hands like when you grab pennies.
pool their pennies, page 366	Explain that when everyone puts all their pennies together in one, big, shared amount or pool, they pool their pennies.
Minute Math+, page 367	A quick math exercise that lasts about a minute in *First Grade Everyday Mathematics* is called *Minute Math*+.

Building Academic Language: Word Familiy *-at*
In this lesson, children work with *flats, mats,* and *patterns*. These words all have the /at/ sound. Because /at/ is spelled and sounds the same in each word, children can predict other words that have this *-at* pattern. In addition, single syllable words like *flats* and *mats* rhyme. *Pattern* is a much bigger word but knowing the sound of *-at* can help a reader figure out its pronunciation too.

Checking for Understanding
Use the prompts below, your own questions, and the master on page 110 to plan comprehension checks for English Learners.

English Proficiency	Prompts
Beginning	*Show how many cubes are equal to one flat.*
Early Intermediate	*How many cubes are equal to one flat?*
Intermediate	*Explain how you know how many cubes equal a flat.*

Providing Access: Using Symbols

In this lesson, children learn the relation symbols used in math. Explain that symbols make it possible for people who speak and understand different languages to understand meanings. Have children brainstorm signs or symbols that they see in school or the community. Discuss how symbols help people know what to do in new situations.

Previewing Vocabulary

An explanation of words with multiple meanings, key math terms, and common procedural vocabulary may aid student comprehension. Consider previewing these terms and reinforcing them as they are used in the lesson.

Words and Phrases	Meanings
wild cards, page 370	Wild cards are playing cards in a deck that can be used as any value a player might need in a card game.
facedown, page 370	Explain that when you lie down on your stomach, your face is down and people cannot tell who you are. When cards are facedown, the numbers are not showing.
handful, page 372	A handful is an amount that will vary from person to person. It is as much as the hand can hold.
half-sheet, page 372	A single piece of paper is called a *sheet of paper*. A piece of paper that is half that size is called a *half-sheet*.

Building Academic Language: Cognates

English Learners who speak a language that shares Greek or Latin roots with English may benefit from learning cognates (words with similar spellings and meanings). Words that end with *-ion* in English share a common root with Spanish words ending in *-ión*. Spanish speakers may benefit from seeing this connection. Add *discussion / discusión* and *relation / relación* to a chart of *-ion* cognates. Look for other words in this lesson to add.

Checking for Understanding

Use the prompts below, your own questions, and the master on page 110 to plan comprehension checks for English Learners.

English Proficiency	Prompts
Beginning	*Draw two nickels and one dime. Compare them to two dimes and one nickel. Which is worth more?*
Early Intermediate	Point to the greater than symbol. *Does this symbol mean greater than or less than?*
Intermediate	Point to the greater than symbol. *Explain how you know whether this symbol is greater than or less than.*

Explorations: Exploring Area, Weight, and Counting

Providing Access: Using Math Tools

In this lesson, children work with a pan balance. Have children compare different objects to find things that weigh the same. Provide English Learners with sentence frames to describe their findings: _____ (object's) weight is the same as _____ (object's). When I remove _____ the _____ side of the pan balance is heavier. When the pan is heavier, it tips _____.

Previewing Vocabulary

An explanation of words with multiple meanings, key math terms, and common procedural vocabulary may aid student comprehension. Consider previewing these terms and reinforcing them as they are used in the lesson.

Words and Phrases	Meanings
gaps, page 375	Spaces between two objects that should touch one another are gaps.
overlap, page 375	Two flat objects overlap when they should typically touch one another along a seam.
desktop, page 376	The flat top surface of a desk used for writing on is the desktop.

Building Academic Language: Homophones

In this lesson, children learn new measurement terminology. Clarify these terms and their homophones for English Learners. *Weigh* sounds the same as *way* but has a different spelling and meaning. Explain the differences between *weight* and *wait*. Make a chart for English Learners to add homophone pairs in English.

Checking for Understanding

Use the prompts below, your own questions, and the master on page 110 to plan comprehension checks for English Learners.

English Proficiency	Prompts
Beginning	*Write the name of the two different units you have selected. Show which of the two units is larger.*
Early Intermediate	*Do these units overlap, or is there a gap?*
Intermediate	*Tell why it is important that there are not gaps or overlaps when measuring.*

Lesson 5·5

Animal Weights

Providing Access: Expanding Vocabulary

This lesson compares the weights of various animals. Some English Learners may only know the English names of the most common animals, such as *dog* and *cat*. A crucial element of building academic language throughout the day is expanding vocabulary in many categories. Have children work in small groups to name each of the animals and categorize them on a chart under the following headings: Fur, Feathers, Scales, and Skin.

Previewing Vocabulary

An explanation of words with multiple meanings, key math terms, and common procedural vocabulary may aid student comprehension. Consider previewing these terms and reinforcing them as they are used in the lesson.

Words and Phrases	Meanings
record, page 380	(v.) *To record* means to write down or make a record of some information. Stress the second syllable in *record* when it is used as a verb.
shaker, page 382	A small container used to shake up something inside is a shaker. A *salt shaker* contains salt to sprinkle out. A *dice shaker* is a cup used to roll out dice.
score, page 383	The total points of each person or team at the end of a game is the score.

Building Academic Language: Abbreviations

In this lesson, children learn that *lb* is the abbreviation for *pound*. Explain that abbreviations stand for longer English words. *St.* stands for *Street* and *CA* stands for *California*. Spanish speakers may know the word for *pound* in Spanish is *libra*. This word knowledge may help them remember the *pound* abbreviation. Look up *pound* in a dictionary to understand the abbreviation.

Checking for Understanding

Use the prompts below, your own questions, and the master on page 110 to plan comprehension checks for English Learners.

English Proficiency	Prompts
Beginning	*Are all animals pets? Can a snake be a pet? Make a picture to show how.*
Early Intermediate	*Does your favorite pet have fur, skin, feathers, or scales?*
Intermediate	*If you could have a pet, what animal would you like to have? Why?*

Copyright © Wright Group/McGraw-Hill

Providing Access: Adding Visual Cues

Number stories can be quite difficult for English Learners because the stories include story language that can be unfamiliar as well as procedural language that can be quite academic. As children create and tell their own number stories, suggest that they illustrate the stories to make them more comprehensible. Encourage children to use math symbols in their pictures as well.

Previewing Vocabulary

An explanation of words with multiple meanings, key math terms, and common procedural vocabulary may aid student comprehension. Consider previewing these terms and reinforcing them as they are used in the lesson.

Words and Phrases	Meanings
zookeeper, page 385	A trained person who cares for animals in a zoo is a zookeeper.
pan balance, page 387	A balance scale that has two flat pans, one on each side, to compare weights of two objects or a collection of objects is a pan balance.
greater than, page 387	In mathematics, the word *greater* is used as "larger," "bigger," or "having more value," different from the descriptive word *great* meaning "fantastic."

Building Academic Language: *Then* and *Than*

Clarify the different meanings of *then* and *than*. Write the words on the board to show the different spellings. Explain the word *then* has to do with time and answers the question "When?" *Then* is spelled like *when*. The word *than* is a comparison word and is used with *more* or *less* in math phrases, such as *5 is more than 2*.

Checking for Understanding

Use the prompts below, your own questions, and the master on page 110 to plan comprehension checks for English Learners.

English Proficiency	Prompts
Beginning	*Point to the animal that weighs more. Make a stack of books that equals the weight of the penguin.*
Early Intermediate	*The beaver weighs 56 pounds—is it heavier or lighter than the penguin?*
Intermediate	*Name the animals in order from heaviest to lightest.*

Providing Access: Creating a Book

Have children work in small groups to create several comparison number stories. One story should answer the question "Who has more?" The other should answer the question "Who has less?" Give each group a math fact to use and art supplies to illustrate. When children are finished, gather their illustrated number stories into a book.

Previewing Vocabulary

An explanation of words with multiple meanings, key math terms, and common procedural vocabulary may aid student comprehension. Consider previewing these terms and reinforcing them as they are used in the lesson.

Words and Phrases	Meanings
count up, page 389	To count to higher numbers is to count up. Explain that to count forward is the opposite of to count down.
the rest, page 390	The amount that is left over is the rest. It is extra or not needed.
not enough left, page 390	This phrase means there is not enough remaining or left over. Children may know the word *left* as a direction word.

Building Academic Language: Comparatives and Superlatives

Help children make comparisons in this lesson. Review this pattern, draw a simple chart, and ask children to add to it:

Positives	Comparatives	Superlatives
little	less	least
some	more	most

Checking for Understanding

Use the prompts below, your own questions, and the master on page 110 to plan comprehension checks for English Learners.

English Proficiency	Prompts
Beginning	*Using two handfuls of pennies, show which handful has more.*
Early Intermediate	*Work with a partner to compare who has more pennies. Tell who has more and who has less pennies.*
Intermediate	*Make a list of the steps to determine who has more when comparing two quantities.*

Solving Number Stories

Providing Access: Acting Out Number Stories

Use role-playing to better engage English Learners in creating and solving number stories. Have children work in small groups to plan and discuss the story line before acting out the story. Role play requires conceptual understanding but less linguistic proficiency than more traditional participation.

Previewing Vocabulary

An explanation of words with multiple meanings, key math terms, and common procedural vocabulary may aid student comprehension. Consider previewing these terms and reinforcing them as they are used in the lesson.

Words and Phrases	Meanings
total, page 395	The final, complete combined amount is the total.
dots, page 395	Small round marks are dots; often they are in a pattern on clothing.
side-by-side, page 397	Lining up objects right next to one another in a row is placing them side-by-side. When objects are side-by-side, it is easy to see which line of objects has more.

Building Academic Language: Irregular Past Tense

Very often number stories report something that has already happened. They use the past tense of verbs to show this. Many verbs in English add an *-ed* on the end to indicate action in the past. However, many past tense verbs are irregular, meaning the base word changes. Make a chart of present/past pairs, such as *buy/bought, find/found, spend/spent, give/gave*, and so on.

Checking for Understanding

Use the prompts below, your own questions, and the master on page 110 to plan comprehension checks for English Learners.

English Proficiency	Prompts
Beginning	*Select the domino with the most dots. Which has the least?*
Early Intermediate	*Listen to a number story and write down the number sentence that represents it.*
Intermediate	*Make up a number story using the names of two students in your class.*

Dice Sums

Providing Access: Cultural Note

In this lesson, the teacher checks children's understanding of frequency by asking why they think the number 7 came up most frequently. One possible answer a child might state is, "Because 7 is a lucky number." Although such cultural lore is not the focus of the lesson, it is an opportunity to explore cultural beliefs about numbers.

Previewing Vocabulary

An explanation of words with multiple meanings, key math terms, and common procedural vocabulary may aid student comprehension. Consider previewing these terms and reinforcing them as they are used in the lesson.

Words and Phrases	Meanings
roll, page 401	To gently toss the dice so that the dice turn over and over to land on a random number is to roll them.
die, page 401	One of a pair of dice is a die. Children may know the verb *die*, but clarify that the object *die* is not related to the meaning of the verb.
die throws, page 401	A roll of one die is a die throw.

Building Academic Language: Irregular Past Tense

Children often report on data and past events. Past tense verbs are used to discuss data that has been collected. Many verbs in English add an *-ed* on the end to show that events occurred in the past. However, many other past tense verbs are irregular, meaning the base word changes. Add to a class chart of present/past pairs. Include *throw/thrown, know/known, come/came, see/saw,* and others from the lesson.

Checking for Understanding

Use the prompts below, your own questions, and the master on page 110 to plan comprehension checks for English Learners.

English Proficiency	Prompts
Beginning	*Point to the number sentence that shows 3 > 2.*
Early Intermediate	*Does this symbol > mean greater than or less than?*
Intermediate	*Compare two numbers with the > symbol. Explain how you did this.*

Turn-Around Facts

Providing Access: Names of Games

Throughout *Everyday Mathematics,* children practice through games. Very often in English, games have names that make them sound fun and make the name more memorable. Point out that *Grab Bag* is almost a palindrome, which is a word, phrase, or sequence of numbers that can be read the same way in either direction. Tell children that the phrase *grab bag* is often used to describe a situation in which you do not know how it will turn out.

Previewing Vocabulary

An explanation of words with multiple meanings, key math terms, and common procedural vocabulary may aid student comprehension. Consider previewing these terms and reinforcing them as they are used in the lesson.

Words and Phrases	Meanings
in common, page 404	To share a similarity is to have something in common.
turn around, page 404	To reverse and go in the opposite direction is to turn around.
right-hand corner, page 405	Explain that when you look down at your hands you see your right hand on the right side of your body. Something is on the right-hand side if it is on the same side as your right hand.

Building Academic Language: Hyphenated Words

Some compound words are hyphenated, such as those in the following phrases: *right-hand corner, left-hand corner,* and *turn-around facts.* In this case, a phrase used as a descriptor is hyphenated to clarify the meaning. For example, a *right-hand corner* is different from a *right hand-corner.* List hyphenated terms from this unit on a chart and add to it throughout the unit.

Checking for Understanding

Use the prompts below, your own questions, and the master on page 110 to plan comprehension checks for English Learners.

English Proficiency	Prompts
Beginning	See TLG p. 407. *Use the on-the-floor number line to show where the Hoppers landed.*
Early Intermediate	See TLG p. 407. *Tell where the Hoppers landed on the number line.*
Intermediate	See TLG p. 407. *Predict where the second Hopper will land on the number line and explain your thinking.*

Easy Facts

Providing Access: Color Coding

Shading number patterns on a number grid provides additional connection between the concept and the language for English Learners. It also allows the teacher to quickly direct children's attention to a row or column of numbers for easy reference and to check children's understanding without relying solely on their English proficiency.

Previewing Vocabulary

An explanation of words with multiple meanings, key math terms, and common procedural vocabulary may aid student comprehension. Consider previewing these terms and reinforcing them as they are used in the lesson.

Words and Phrases	Meanings
Beat the Calculator, page 411	In this context, *beat* means to go faster than the calculator and find the answer before the calculator does.
"Brains," page 411	The players in the *Beat the Calculator* game that rely on their thinking to solve the fact problems are the "Brains," because they do the problem in their heads.

Building Academic Language: Nouns and Verbs

In this lesson, children play *Beat the Calculator.* In English, often the work a person does is indicated by their job title. For example, a person who teaches is called a teacher. In this game, the person who calls the facts is the "Caller." Adding *-er* to the end of the action sometimes forms the name of the job. Add other examples to a jobs list.

Checking for Understanding

Use the prompts below, your own questions, and the master on page 110 to plan comprehension checks for English Learners.

English Proficiency	Prompts
Beginning	*Point to the +0 facts on the Facts Table. Shade them blue.*
Early Intermediate	*Find a pattern on the Facts Table and shade it. What is the pattern?*
Intermediate	*Describe the location of the double facts on the Facts Table.*

Providing Access: Using Puppets

In U.S. schools, teachers often use questions to help children think and form independent conclusions. Some children may be puzzled to hear a teacher ask questions for which the teacher should know the answer. Help children become more familiar with the teacher-student interaction pattern of using questions and answers. For example, introduce the "What's My Rule?" routine using a puppet to ask the questions.

Previewing Vocabulary

An explanation of words with multiple meanings, key math terms, and common procedural vocabulary may aid student comprehension. Consider previewing these terms and reinforcing them as they are used in the lesson.

Words and Phrases	Meanings
guessing game, page 415	A game that uses clues and questions for the players to come up with the answer is a guessing game.
say the magic word, page 415	Magicians often ask the audience to say the magic word, which is usually *abracadabra*. The understanding is that magic will occur after saying the magic word.
predict, page 415	To guess what will occur based on what is known is to predict.

Building Academic Language: Contractions

In this unit and throughout *Everyday Mathematics*, children use the "What's My Rule?" routine. Some English Learners may not realize that the contraction *what's* is another way to say "what is." Point out the apostrophe in the word *what's* and write the word on the board so children can see that *what is* and *what's* are equivalent.

Checking for Understanding

Use the prompts below, your own questions, and the master on page 110 to plan comprehension checks for English Learners.

English Proficiency	Prompts
Beginning	*Point to the machine that gets bigger by 10.*
Early Intermediate	*If the "in" number gets bigger by 10, then what is the rule?*
Intermediate	*Explain how "What's My Rule?" works.*

Applying Rules

Providing Access: Using Signals

To make sure that English Learners of early proficiency levels grasp concepts, check for understanding throughout the lesson. Encourage children with limited English proficiency to indicate their answer by modeling the answer with manipulatives or by using signals, such as thumbs-up, thumbs-down, or head nod.

Previewing Vocabulary

An explanation of words with multiple meanings, key math terms, and common procedural vocabulary may aid student comprehension. Consider previewing these terms and reinforcing them as they are used in the lesson.

Words and Phrases	Meanings
rules, page 420	Instructions that tell you what to do or what not to do are rules.
table, page 420	A table is a graphic representation of data. Children may know the everyday meaning of *table* as furniture.
trade, page 421	To exchange is to trade or to give something and get something else back in return.

Building Academic Language: Compound Words

In this lesson, children learn two new compound words. The number data put into the function machine is called *input,* and the data that comes out of the machine is called *output.* Both *input* and *output* are made up of small words that retain their meaning. Other compound words in this lesson are *follow-up, whenever,* and *overhead.* Add these to a class list of compound words.

Checking for Understanding

Use the prompts below, your own questions, and the master on page 110 to plan comprehension checks for English Learners.

English Proficiency	Prompts
Beginning	*Draw a function machine. Where does the input go? Where does the output go?*
Early Intermediate	*Is this number the input or the output? The input is what you put _____ to the machine. The output is what comes _____ of the machine.*
Intermediate	*Describe how the function machine works.*

The Addition/Subtraction Facts Table

Providing Access: Using Graphic Organizers

Hands-on learning deepens English Learners' conceptual understanding and provides them with an alternate way to demonstrate their understanding. Create a table with 11 columns (labeled 2–12). Have children sort and chart domino sums into the column labeled with the corresponding sum.

Previewing Vocabulary

An explanation of words with multiple meanings, key math terms, and common procedural vocabulary may aid student comprehension. Consider previewing these terms and reinforcing them as they are used in the lesson.

Words and Phrases	Meanings
take turns, page 537	When playing with others, you often wait for your turn while they take theirs. You then take your turn after they are done.
turn-around, page 537	Explain the everyday meaning of *turn around* is to reverse and go in the other direction. Have children act out walking and then turning around.
a roll, page 541	A roll is when you gently toss the dice so that the dice turn over and over to land on a random number.

Building Academic Language: Nouns and Verbs

Look for terms that children may know as nouns, but are used as verbs. For example, in this lesson the following words are used as verbs: *record, order, sequence,* and *label.* Have children consider whether the word represents an action or an object. Keep a list of such words.

VERBS describe an action.	NOUNS describe a person, place, or thing.
[to] record	[a] record
[to] throw	[a] throw
[to] chart	[a] chart

Checking for Understanding

Use the prompts below, your own questions, and the master on page 110 to plan comprehension checks for English Learners.

English Proficiency	Prompts
Beginning	*Sort the domino sums in counting order: 1, 2, 3, 4...*
Early Intermediate	*Three categories of domino sums are blank, _____, and _____.*
Intermediate	*Explain to another student how to figure out what category each domino belongs in.*

Providing Access: Building Background

Write different names and titles on sentence strips, for example, teacher, (your name), coach, and mom to demonstrate that one person can have many different names. Let several children stand and share their many different names. Explain that these are equivalent names because they name the same person. Tell children that they will work with equivalent names for numbers.

Previewing Vocabulary

An explanation of words with multiple meanings, key math terms, and common procedural vocabulary may aid student comprehension. Consider previewing these terms and reinforcing them as they are used in the lesson.

Words and Phrases	Meanings
sign, page 544	A sign is a symbol that stands for something. An equal sign tells you two quantities are equal. A stop sign tells you to stop.
identical, page 544	Two or more objects that are the same are identical.
half-sheet, page 546	A single piece of paper is called a *sheet of paper*. A piece of paper that is half that size is called a *half-sheet*.

Building Academic Language: Cognates

Expand English Learners' academic vocabulary by pointing out cognates (words with similar spellings and meanings across languages). Tell children the word *equivalent* is *equivalente* in Spanish.

Checking for Understanding

Use the prompts below, your own questions, and the master on page 110 to plan comprehension checks for English Learners.

English Proficiency	Prompts
Beginning	*Write a number equivalent to 2 + 3.*
Early Intermediate	*What is the difference between a number model with the equal sign on the right-hand side and a number model with the equal sign on the left-hand side?*
Intermediate	*What does equivalent mean?*

Fact Families

Providing Access: Connecting Concepts to Familiar Experiences

Explain that the members of a family are related to one another. Have children make a list of their family members. Tell children that in fact families, the numbers are related, and that relation symbols, like the equal sign, are used to show how the numbers are related. Fact families show the relationship between addition and subtraction.

Previewing Vocabulary

An explanation of words with multiple meanings, key math terms, and common procedural vocabulary may aid student comprehension. Consider previewing these terms and reinforcing them as they are used in the lesson.

Words and Phrases	Meanings
guess, page 549	To offer an answer without knowing all the facts is to guess.
rotate, page 550	To turn something in a different direction is to rotate it.
doubles, page 551	The sum of a 1-digit number added to itself is a double, for example, $4 + 4 = 8$.

Building Academic Language: Cognates

English Learners who speak a language that shares roots with English may benefit from learning cognates (words with similar spellings and meanings). For example, words that end with -ble in English share a common root with Spanish words ending in -ble. Add double/doble, probable/probable, and comparable/comparable to a chart of cognates. Look for other words in this lesson to add.

Checking for Understanding

Use the prompts below, your own questions, and the master on page 110 to plan comprehension checks for English Learners.

English Proficiency	Prompts
Beginning	Select four dominos that belong to the same fact family.
Early Intermediate	A family of related number facts is called a fact _____.
Intermediate	Summarize how many addition and subtraction facts are found in a doubles fact family.

Fact Triangles

Providing Access: Words with Multiple Meanings

In English, there are many words that have multiple meanings. The meaning of a word depends on how the word is being used. For example, in this lesson children play *Beat the Calculator*. The word *beat* can mean to hit hard, as in to beat a rug. In the context of the game, *beat* means to come up with an answer before the calculator does. Discuss other directions that have words with double meanings, such as *check* your answer and *draw* a card.

Previewing Vocabulary

An explanation of words with multiple meanings, key math terms, and common procedural vocabulary may aid student comprehension. Consider previewing these terms and reinforcing them as they are used in the lesson.

Words and Phrases	Meanings
format, page 554	The style, or way, in which something is set up is the format.
initials, page 556	The first letters of your first name and last name are your initials.
land, page 556	In a board game, when a game piece stops and comes to rest on a spot or place, it lands on that place.

Building Academic Language: Nouns and Verbs

In English, often the work that people do is described by their job title. For example, a person who teaches is a teacher. In *Beat the Calculator,* the person who calls the facts is the "Caller." The "Brain" thinks through the answer, so that child is a thinker. Often, adding *-er* to the end of the verb forms the word that describes the job. Find other examples and add them to a jobs list.

Checking for Understanding

Use the prompts below, your own questions, and the master on page 110 to plan comprehension checks for English Learners.

English Proficiency	Prompts
Beginning	*Draw a Fact Triangle that has only one addition and one subtraction fact.*
Early Intermediate	*What do you call a fact family with two digits that are the same?*
Intermediate	*Explain how to play the* Fact Power Game.

Providing Access: Using Alliteration

Throughout *Everyday Mathematics,* children practice through games. Often, games have names that use alliteration to make them sound fun and to make the name more memorable. In this unit, children work with *Tric-Trac* and *Penny Plate.* Both words in each title begin with the same letter sounds. Ask children to name other game titles with alliteration.

Previewing Vocabulary

An explanation of words with multiple meanings, key math terms, and common procedural vocabulary may aid student comprehension. Consider previewing these terms and reinforcing them as they are used in the lesson.

Words and Phrases	Meanings
table, page 560	Children may know the everyday meaning of *table* as furniture. A graphic representation of data is a table.
figure out, page 560	To solve a problem and determine (or get) the answer is to figure it out.
find the total, page 562	To compute, to determine (or get) the total is to find the total. You may want to discuss how this is related to the everyday meaning of *find,* which is to go look for something.

Building Academic Language: Pronunciation

As English Learners work hard to listen to and understand English, it is very important that teachers speak clearly and articulate words carefully, especially when pronouncing words that end with the letters *ty.* For example, the words *forty* and *fifty* often sound like *four-dee, fif-dee.* Also, in this lesson, the words *Facts Table* may blend together to sound like "fac-stable." Pause slightly between words so children know where the break is.

Checking for Understanding

Use the prompts below, your own questions, and the master on page 110 to plan comprehension checks for English Learners.

English Proficiency	Prompts
Beginning	*Use the Facts Table to show 7 – 3. Add to check your answer.*
Early Intermediate	*Use the Facts Table to find the answer to 7 – 3. What is the difference?*
Intermediate	*Tell how you can check a subtraction answer using addition.*

Providing Access: Cultural Note

The metric system is used in most parts of the world so English Learners whose families have lived outside the United States may know it well. Encourage families to lend any metric measuring tools, such as a bathroom scale or meterstick, to the class.

Previewing Vocabulary

An explanation of words with multiple meanings, key math terms, and common procedural vocabulary may aid student comprehension. Consider previewing these terms and reinforcing them as they are used in the lesson.

Words and Phrases	Meanings
consecutive, page 565	Two or more in a row, such as two centimeter marks on a ruler, are consecutive.
halfway, page 565	Halfway is in the middle. Show children the mark between two specific centimeter marks on a ruler. Describe it as a halfway mark.
end-to-end, page 565	Explain that placing the end of one object next to another so that the seam is touching but not overlapping is end-to-end.

Building Academic Language: Hard and Soft *c*

In English, the letter *c* makes different sounds depending on the letters that surround it. English Learners who speak Spanish are familiar with the hard and soft *c*. It is a transferable skill from Spanish to English. Add words to the following chart:

Hard *c* sounds like /k/ when followed by *a, o,* or *u.*	Soft *c* sounds like /s/ when followed by *e, i,* or *y.*
can	cent
coin	centimeter
count	cycle
cut	dice

Checking for Understanding

Use the prompts below, your own questions, and the master on page 110 to plan comprehension checks for English Learners.

English Proficiency	Prompts
Beginning	*Point to the halfway mark on the ruler.*
Early Intermediate	*How long is a centimeter ruler? What is the halfway mark?*
Intermediate	*Explain why an object measures differently with inches than with centimeters.*

Providing Access: Color Coding

Shading number patterns on a number grid provides additional connection between the concept and the language for English Learners. It also allows the teacher to quickly direct children's attention to a row or column of numbers and to check children's understanding without relying solely on their English proficiency. In this lesson, children show even and odd numbers by color-coding them on a number grid.

Previewing Vocabulary

An explanation of words with multiple meanings, key math terms, and common procedural vocabulary may aid student comprehension. Consider previewing these terms and reinforcing them as they are used in the lesson.

Words and Phrases	Meanings
alike, page 570	Things that are alike are similar to one another.
egg cartons, page 571	The long, cardboard box with 12 cups to hold eggs safely from getting broken is an egg carton. Show children an example.
cups, page 573	The spaces where the eggs sit in the egg carton are cups.

Building Academic Language: Nontransferable Skill—Final /t/

Sometimes English Learners have a difficult time perceiving and pronouncing English sounds that do not exist in their home language. In this lesson, children work with Fact Triangles. The ending sound of the word *fact* may be difficult for some children to pronounce if it is not used in the final position of words in their home language. Be sure to model and enunciate *fact* carefully, especially when it comes before *triangles*.

Checking for Understanding

Use the prompts below, your own questions, and the master on page 110 to plan comprehension checks for English Learners.

English Proficiency	Prompts
Beginning	*Make three different triangles on your geoboard.*
Early Intermediate	*Tell if your triangle points up, down, right, or left.*
Intermediate	*Describe how your triangles are different and how they are alike.*

Providing Access: Restating

English Learners new to your class may need extra help with the math terminology. For example, a statement like, "Figure out the missing input numbers," has a number of potentially unfamiliar phrases. Rephrase such statements. Substitute "find the answer to," for "figure out." Restate "the missing input numbers" as "the numbers that are not there," or "the numbers we need to put into the machine to make the rule work."

Previewing Vocabulary

An explanation of words with multiple meanings, key math terms, and common procedural vocabulary may aid student comprehension. Consider previewing these terms and reinforcing them as they are used in the lesson.

Words and Phrases	Meanings
input, page 575	Something you put into the machine is called *input*
output, page 576	Something that comes out of the machine is called *output*.
replace, page 576	To put something in the place of another thing is to replace it.

Building Academic Language: Contractions

In this lesson and throughout *Everyday Mathematics*, children engage in the "What's My Rule?" routine. Some English Learners may not realize that the contraction *what's* is another way to say "what is." Point out the apostrophe in the word *what's* and write the word on the board so children can see that *what is* and *what's* are equivalent.

Checking for Understanding

Use the prompts below, your own questions, and the master on page 110 to plan comprehension checks for English Learners.

English Proficiency	Prompts
Beginning	*Write in the missing input numbers.*
Early Intermediate	*Does the output go into the machine or come out of the machine?*
Intermediate	*How do you figure out which is the output and which is the input?*

Quarters

Providing Access: Internet Resources

Provide background information and interactive support for English Learners with Internet resources. For example, U.S. currency information on minting coins is available at the U.S. Department of the Treasury Web site for Education. Visit www.usmint.gov.

Previewing Vocabulary

An explanation of words with multiple meanings, key math terms, and common procedural vocabulary may aid student comprehension. Consider previewing these terms and reinforcing them as they are used in the lesson.

Words and Phrases	Meanings
birth, page 581	The anniversary of the day someone is born is their birthday.
tails, page 581	*Tails* refers to the opposite side of heads on a U.S. coin. This side has a famous place or scene stamped on it.
heads, page 581	The side of a U.S. coin that has a portrait of a famous person stamped on it is called *heads*.

Building Academic Language: Words with *qu-*

In this lesson, children learn about quarters. For some English Learners the letter *q* may be an unfamiliar alphabet letter and /kw/ an unfamiliar sound. For speakers of Spanish, the /kw/ sound exists but is spelled *cua-* as in *cuartos*. Practice pronunciation by reciting the following sentence with children: *The queen requested a quarter and asked this question, "How many pennies does a quarter equal?"*

Checking for Understanding

Use the prompts below, your own questions, and the master on page 110 to plan comprehension checks for English Learners.

English Proficiency	Prompts
Beginning	*Show the heads and tails on a quarter.*
Early Intermediate	*How much is a quarter worth? Name three coins that together add up to one quarter.*
Intermediate	*Why is a quarter called a "quarter"?*

Digital Clocks

Providing Access: Using Graphic Organizers

When working with English Learners, teachers face the challenge of making the lesson rigorous and comprehensible. Graphic organizers promote higher-level thinking by helping children compare, contrast, and organize data without requiring high levels of English proficiency. In this lesson, children explore the differences between an analog clock and a digital clock. Use a Venn diagram to show the similarities and differences.

Previewing Vocabulary

An explanation of words with multiple meanings, key math terms, and common procedural vocabulary may aid student comprehension. Consider previewing these terms and reinforcing them as they are used in the lesson.

Words and Phrases	Meanings
analog clock, page 589	An analog clock displays the time with an hour hand and minute hand on the clock face.
digital clock, page 589	A digital clock displays the time with numbers.
colon, page 590	Explain that when writing the time you separate the hour and minutes by the punctuation mark called a *colon*.

Building Academic Language: Cognates

Children learned that multisyllabic words in English that end with *-al*, such as *digital, visual, total,* and *diagonal,* have the same spellings and meanings in Spanish. Throughout the unit, capture other *-al* words in English to list in a word chart. Remember that single syllable words like *pal* do not fit this cognate pattern.

Checking for Understanding

Use the prompts below, your own questions, and the master on page 110 to plan comprehension checks for English Learners.

English Proficiency	Prompts
Beginning	*Draw a digital clock and display the time on it.*
Early Intermediate	*Is this an analog or digital clock?*
Intermediate	*What is the difference between an analog and digital clock?*

Introducing *My Reference Book*

Providing Access: Using Reference Books

English Learners may benefit from looking up words in a bilingual dictionary. Many of the words in the unit vocabulary list are cognates with Spanish. This connection may enhance Spanish speakers' retention of new mathematics terminology. The *Everyday Mathematics My Reference Book* is also an excellent resource for all English Learners because it includes illustrative examples of the new concepts and skills.

Previewing Vocabulary

An explanation of words with multiple meanings, key math terms, and common procedural vocabulary may aid student comprehension. Consider previewing these terms and reinforcing them as they are used in the lesson.

Words and Phrases	Meanings
table of contents, page 594	A table of contents is a list of the topics in a book and the corresponding page numbers.
scavenger hunt, page 595	This is a game that includes a list of odd or unusual objects that the players must find and collect.
ordering, page 596	In this context, *ordering* means sorting and putting objects or numbers in sequential order.

Building Academic Language: Alphabetical Order

Many reference books are set up in alphabetical order. The index in *My Reference Book* lists terms alphabetically. Help children use the index to find the words *squares, tally chart,* and *triangles.* Discuss how the arrangement of words in alphabetical order helps to find the words quickly.

Checking for Understanding

Use the prompts below, your own questions, and the master on page 110 to plan comprehension checks for English Learners.

English Proficiency	Prompts
Beginning	*Find the Table of Contents. What page does the Index begin on?*
Early Intermediate	*What part of the book is in alphabetical order?*
Intermediate	*How does the Table of Contents help you find the information you need?*

Data Landmarks

Providing Access: Role-Playing New Concepts

In this lesson, children learn the meaning of several data landmarks. To help English Learners better understand the concept and remember the terminology, have children act out the median. Children bring their slates as they form a line in order from smallest to largest number. Two children who have the same number stand next to each other. Children at each end sit down. Repeat until just the middle value remains.

Previewing Vocabulary

An explanation of words with multiple meanings, key math terms, and common procedural vocabulary may aid student comprehension. Consider previewing these terms and reinforcing them as they are used in the lesson.

Words and Phrases	Meanings
count higher, page 599	Explain that to count to larger numbers is to count higher.
at this stage, page 599	Explain that another way to say this is "at this point in the sequence."

Building Academic Language: Comparatives and Superlatives

In this lesson, children compare data from their calculator count. They need to know how to describe the largest and smallest numbers. Revisit the class comparison chart and work with children to collect comparison words and add them to the chart.

Positives	Comparatives	Superlatives
high	higher	highest
large	larger	largest
small	smaller	smallest

Checking for Understanding

Use the prompts below, your own questions, and the master on page 110 to plan comprehension checks for English Learners.

English Proficiency	Prompts
Beginning	Point to the median number.
Early Intermediate	Is the middle value called the "range" or the "median"?
Intermediate	What is the median?

Attribute Rules

Providing Access: Language Practice through Games

In this lesson, children play *Make My Design*. This helps English Learners practice using description. Two children face in opposite directions. The first player creates a pattern and uses only words to describe it. The other player recreates the design based on the description. Then, players switch roles. Before children begin, brainstorm a list of descriptive words and phrases that might be useful.

Previewing Vocabulary

An explanation of words with multiple meanings, key math terms, and common procedural vocabulary may aid student comprehension. Consider previewing these terms and reinforcing them as they are used in the lesson.

Words and Phrases	Meanings
sort, page 623	To separate into categories based on common characteristic(s), such as color or shape, is to sort.
in common, page 623	To share things that are the same is to have something in common.
blocks, page 623	Some English Learners may know the word *block* to mean street. Here, *blocks* are 3-dimensional shapes used for math.

Building Academic Language: Attribute Adjectives

Children do not regularly use description until higher-proficiency levels of English. In this lesson, children work with attribute blocks. Create a large, four-column chart and list descriptive words under the headings: Size, Shape, Color, and Other.

Checking for Understanding

Use the prompts below, your own questions, and the master on page 110 to plan comprehension checks for English Learners.

English Proficiency	Prompts
Beginning	*Show me a round, red block.*
Early Intermediate	*Is this round or not? What shape is this?*
Intermediate	*How would you describe this shape?*

Explorations: Exploring Attributes, Designs, and Fact Platters

Providing Access: Using Graphic Organizers

In this lesson, children continue to work with attribute blocks, which is an ideal opportunity for all children to extend their descriptive vocabulary. Use a word web or add to the four-column chart from Lesson 7.1 of this handbook. Add words that describe shape, color, size, and other attributes. Encourage children to refer to the chart during lesson activities.

Previewing Vocabulary

An explanation of words with multiple meanings, key math terms, and common procedural vocabulary may aid student comprehension. Consider previewing these terms and reinforcing them as they are used in the lesson.

Words and Phrases	Meanings
guess the rule, page 628	To use clues and what you know to try to figure out the rule is to guess the rule.
the secret rule, page 628	The rule that is not known is the secret rule. Only the teacher knows what the secret rule is.
a given design, page 629	The word *given* in this phrase describes a design that will be given to the child as a model. It does not refer to one particular design.

Building Academic Language: Silent *g*

In this lesson, children work with creating designs with attribute blocks. Point out that the word *design* has the word *sign* in it. The *g* is silent in *sign* and *design*. Explain that when *g* and *n* are together in the same syllable, the *g* is silent. Find other words with a silent *g* and add them to a word list.

Checking for Understanding

Use the prompts below, your own questions, and the master on page 110 to plan comprehension checks for English Learners.

English Proficiency	Prompts
Beginning	*Sort the attribute blocks into three groups.*
Early Intermediate	*Which attribute category has the most blocks?*
Intermediate	*How do you decide which categories to use when sorting blocks?*

Providing Access: Using Physical Models

To provide experience with identifying pattern-block shapes, have children use their fingers to draw a pattern-block shape on another child's back. Children try to guess the shape. Have them take turns drawing and guessing pattern-block shapes.

Previewing Vocabulary

An explanation of words with multiple meanings, key math terms, and common procedural vocabulary may aid student comprehension. Consider previewing these terms and reinforcing them as they are used in the lesson.

Words and Phrases	Meanings
corners, page 635	Children may know *street corners* or other everyday uses of the word *corners*. Help them link this to the mathematical meaning of the point where two lines meet.
sides, page 635	Children may know phrases with *side*, such as *off sides* and *take sides*. In this lesson, a *side* refers to a line segment in a polygon.
least, page 637	The smallest amount when comparing two or more amounts is the least.

Building Academic Language: Cognates

In this unit on geometry and attributes, Spanish speakers will find many words that are similar in English and Spanish. Geometric figures that end with *-angle* in English, end with *-ángulo* in Spanish, for example, *triangle* and *triángulo*. Words that end with *-gon* in English end with *-gono* in Spanish, for example, *hexagon* and *hexágono*. Collect other examples in a two-column chart.

Checking for Understanding

Use the prompts below, your own questions, and the master on page 110 to plan comprehension checks for English Learners.

English Proficiency	Prompts
Beginning	*Point to a side of the square. Point to a corner of the square.*
Early Intermediate	*Find an object that has a square corner and tell the name of that object.*
Intermediate	*Is a street corner a square corner? Why?*

Making Polygons

Providing Access: Hands-on Modeling

To help children learn polygon shapes and their characteristics, have them construct polygons out of straws. Instruction is less abstract and more comprehensible when English Learners are involved visually and physically. For example, children can see and feel what *straight* means by using the straws to construct polygons.

Previewing Vocabulary

An explanation of words with multiple meanings, key math terms, and common procedural vocabulary may aid student comprehension. Consider previewing these terms and reinforcing them as they are used in the lesson.

Words and Phrases	Meanings
trace the shapes, page 639	To trace the shape is to use your pointer finger to outline it.
gaps, page 639	Explain that when the sides of a shape are connected, there are no open spaces called *gaps* between them.
flipping coins, page 641	Explain that when people want to settle a question, they might flip a coin; this is sometimes called a coin toss. The coin turns many times in the air and lands on one side, showing either heads or tails.

Building Academic Language: Nontransferable Skill—Final /p/

The word *flip* ends with the sound /p/, which is not an ending sound in many languages. The English sound /p/ is strongly aspirated, that is, accompanied by an audible breath, making it difficult to pronounce. English Learners tend to approximate new sounds. Spanish speakers might use a softer sound, almost like a /b/. Demonstrate the /p/ sound by placing a piece of paper in front of your mouth to show the force of the air.

Checking for Understanding

Use the prompts below, your own questions, and the master on page 110 to plan comprehension checks for English Learners.

English Proficiency	Prompts
Beginning	*Use straws to make a rhombus.*
Early Intermediate	*How many sides does the rhombus have? Is it an open or closed figure?*
Intermediate	*Select a polygon and name three things that have the same shape as the polygon.*

Spheres, Cylinders, and Rectangular Prisms

Providing Access: Using Gestures

Teachers of English Learners often use gestures to provide context clues. Teach children to demonstrate the word *curve* by holding their arms in front of them as though they were holding a large ball. Show *round* by drawing a round figure in the air while saying "round."

Previewing Vocabulary

An explanation of words with multiple meanings, key math terms, and common procedural vocabulary may aid student comprehension. Consider previewing these terms and reinforcing them as they are used in the lesson.

Words and Phrases	Meanings
faces, page 646	English Learners may be familiar with the word *face,* but in this context, it refers to the flat side of shapes. Children may find it helpful to say "flat face" when talking about shapes.
plane, page 648	Children may know the word *plane* as in *airplane* or the homophone *plain.* Here, it refers to a flat 2-dimensional shape.
almost, page 647	Explain that when something is not exact but very close to the ideal, the word *almost* is used to describe it.

Building Academic Language: The Sounds of *sph-* and *cy-*

In this lesson, children learn the formal names of shapes, including a *sphere.* English Learners may not be familiar with the /sf/ sound made by *sph-*. Remind children that *ph-* makes the /f/ sound as in *phone,* so adding the /s/ sound to the beginning creates the sound in *sph-*. The word *cylinder* also starts with a /s/ sound. Revisit the chart on hard and soft *c* from Lesson 2.8 of this handbook and add words spelled *cy-* from this lesson.

Checking for Understanding

Use the prompts below, your own questions, and the master on page 110 to plan comprehension checks for English Learners.

English Proficiency	Prompts
Beginning	*Point out three things in the classroom that are almost rectangular prisms.*
Early Intermediate	*Is a book more like a cylinder or a rectangular prism?*
Intermediate	*Name one thing in the classroom that is a sphere, one that is a cylinder, and one that is a rectangular prism.*

Pyramids, Cones, and Cubes

Providing Access: Working in Partnerships

When children work together, they increase their vocabulary and may participate more freely. Have children work in partnerships to answer the Math Message and name an object that is shaped like a cone. Consider pairing two children who know the same home language but are at different levels of English proficiency. English Learners may be familiar with such objects as ice cream cones and party hats but not know the words in English. Have children draw a picture if neither partner knows the names.

Previewing Vocabulary

An explanation of words with multiple meanings, key math terms, and common procedural vocabulary may aid student comprehension. Consider previewing these terms and reinforcing them as they are used in the lesson.

Words and Phrases	Meanings
comes to a point, page 650	Explain that something gets smaller until it comes to a single point, like the letter *v*. This phrase is also used when someone is speaking and rambles without clearly stating their message. People wish the person would come to a point.
take a turn, page 653	Explain that when you play with others, you often wait for your turn while they take theirs. Then you take a turn.

Building Academic Language: Silent *e*

In English, the most common silent letter is the silent *e* that ends some words. Point out the silent *e* in *cone* and *cube* from this lesson. Explain that a silent *e* at the end of a word means the sound of *e* is not pronounced. However, without the silent *e*, *cube* would be *cub* and *cone* would be *con*. Have English Learners collect other silent *e* words.

Checking for Understanding

Use the prompts below, your own questions, and the master on page 110 to plan comprehension checks for English Learners.

English Proficiency	Prompts
Beginning	*Point to a figure that has a point.*
Early Intermediate	*Which shape is like a ball—a pyramid or a sphere?*
Intermediate	*Describe what a pyramid feels like.*

Providing Access: Hands-on Examples

In this lesson, children learn about symmetry by folding and cutting shapes in paper. Hands-on activities involve English Learners in fun concept development and provide ample opportunities for building vocabulary. Interacting with concrete materials helps children retain the concepts and the vocabulary.

Previewing Vocabulary

An explanation of words with multiple meanings, key math terms, and common procedural vocabulary may aid student comprehension. Consider previewing these terms and reinforcing them as they are used in the lesson.

Words and Phrases	Meanings
halves, page 655	The plural of *half* is *halves*. In English, /fs/ is not an ending sound in words. It changes to /vs/. *Halves* sounds like *haves*. Help children notice the silent *l* in *halves*.
the cut-out piece, page 656	Explain that this is the paper shape that was cut from the paper. The hyphen shows that the words *cut* and *out* go together.
in nature, page 657	Things in nature are found in natural settings, such as in the sky, ocean, or forest.

Building Academic Language: Prefixes

As children work with symmetrical figures, they fold and unfold paper. Show English Learners that they already know the base word *fold* and by recognizing the prefix *un-*, they can determine the meaning of the word *unfold*. Find other word pairs that use the prefix *un-* to create a word with the opposite meaning, for example, *even/uneven*.

Checking for Understanding

Use the prompts below, your own questions, and the master on page 110 to plan comprehension checks for English Learners.

English Proficiency	Prompts
Beginning	*Are your hands symmetrical? Show a cut-out shape that is symmetrical.*
Early Intermediate	*Is this paper folded or unfolded? Show how you know.*
Intermediate	*Is this paper folded or unfolded? Tell how you know.*

Providing Access: Creating Riddles

Have children demonstrate their understanding of counting coin combinations by solving coin riddles and making up their own riddles for classmates to solve. English Learners draw a picture and then work with another child to write the riddle. Use *Math Masters,* page 223 as a model. Share a template for creating a riddle. Ask: *Who? Took what action? What is the result?*

Previewing Vocabulary

An explanation of words with multiple meanings, key math terms, and common procedural vocabulary may aid student comprehension. Consider previewing these terms and reinforcing them as they are used in the lesson.

Words and Phrases	Meanings
groups of like coins, page 677	This expression means to put coins that are alike in groups. For example, put all the quarters in one group and the pennies in another.
lands on, page 679	When a spinner stops turning, it is pointing to a space on the spinner base. It lands on a color on the spinner.
switch roles, page 681	Explain that to exchange jobs with another person so that person does your job and you do his or her job is to switch roles.

Building Academic Language: Double Consonants

In English, many words have double consonants. Write the words with double consonants from this lesson (*spinner, tally, collect, class,* and *middle*) on a list and ask children to add to it. Circle the double consonants and say the words. In English, double consonants are pronounced as if they were a single letter. Note that in Spanish and some other languages, *rr* and *ll* have a different pronunciation than the single *r* and *l*.

Checking for Understanding

Use the prompts below, your own questions, and the master on page 110 to plan comprehension checks for English Learners.

English Proficiency	Prompts
Beginning	*Show fifteen cents with the fewest coins. Show ten cents with the most possible coins.*
Early Intermediate	*Would you rather have the most coins or the fewest coins? Is it more important to have the most coins or the largest coins?*
Intermediate	*How are the nickel and quarter different? Similar?*

Providing Access: Using Real Objects

Have children use money or money replicas to practice making change. English Learners who have lived outside the United States may be unfamiliar with U.S. coins and bills and will benefit from opportunities to explore and use real coins.

Previewing Vocabulary

An explanation of words with multiple meanings, key math terms, and common procedural vocabulary may aid student comprehension. Consider previewing these terms and reinforcing them as they are used in the lesson.

Words and Phrases	Meanings
serial number, page 683	English Learners may know the homophone *cereal*. Here, a serial number is a number given to a dollar to identify or keep track of it.
bill, page 683	Explain that this word has multiple meanings. In this lesson, it refers to currency, such as a dollar bill, which can be used to pay bills.

Building Academic Language: Vernacular

Young children may have heard various terms for money that are widely used but not usually taught in school. Understanding common idiomatic speech is part of building language proficiency. Words like *moola, bucks, bread*, and *green stuff* are used widely. Explain that these slang terms are not used in mathematics.

Checking for Understanding

Use the prompts below, your own questions, and the master on page 110 to plan comprehension checks for English Learners.

English Proficiency	Prompts
Beginning	*What word do we use for paper money?*
Early Intermediate	*Would you rather have $35 in coins or 2 dollar bills? Would you change your choice if you had to carry them with you all day in your pants pocket?*
Intermediate	*Why do people carry paper money instead of all coins?*

Place Value: Hundreds, Tens, and Ones

Providing Access: Practicing with Games

Games hone math skills and are an excellent context for authentic language practice. Form partnerships to best meet children's needs. For example, a partnership of English Learners who speak the same home language enables them to converse fluently and gain a deeper understanding. A partnership of an English Learner with a child proficient in English provides the learner with English pronunciation models and practice.

Previewing Vocabulary

An explanation of words with multiple meanings, key math terms, and common procedural vocabulary may aid student comprehension. Consider previewing these terms and reinforcing them as they are used in the lesson.

Words and Phrases	Meanings
exchange, page 689	Explain that the word *exchange* has a related meaning to *change*. Each side gives and gets something in an exchange.
ordering, page 692	English Learners may know the word *ordering* from ordering food. Here, it means to put numbers in sequential order.

Building Academic Language: Game Names

Throughout *Everyday Mathematics,* children practice through games. Often, in English, games have names that use alliteration to make them sound fun and to make the name more memorable. In this unit, children play *Tric-Trac*. This is an example of alliteration because both words begin with the same letter sound. Ask children to name other game titles that use alliteration.

Checking for Understanding

Use the prompts below, your own questions, and the master on page 110 to plan comprehension checks for English Learners.

English Proficiency	Prompts
Beginning	*Give thumbs-up if this is the hundreds place.*
Early Intermediate	*Point to each place and say its name.*
Intermediate	*Explain how the Place-Value Mat works.*

Providing Access: Making up Stories

An excellent way for English Learners to understand number stories is to create number stories themselves. English Learners of early proficiency levels may benefit from using sentence frames. Also, support English Learners by encouraging them to first draw pictures and label them on a storyboard.

Previewing Vocabulary

An explanation of words with multiple meanings, key math terms, and common procedural vocabulary may aid student comprehension. Consider previewing these terms and reinforcing them as they are used in the lesson.

Words and Phrases	Meanings
poster, page 694	A poster is a large sign that is posted or hung up on a post to share information.
transparency, page 694	Explain that a clear, transparent sheet you write on and project on an overhead projector for everyone to see is a transparency.
make up [a story], page 696	The words *make up* mean to create or invent fiction. Here, *make up* is an action, which is different from *makeup*, which is cosmetics.

Building Academic Language: Expanding Vocabulary

Build vocabulary when working with number stories. Work with a small group of children to brainstorm words for a number story line. For example, if the story is about going to the store, name words such as *shelf, price tag, bin,* and *shopping cart*. If the story is about school, include *books, binders, backpack, shelves,* and *playground*.

Checking for Understanding

Use the prompts below, your own questions, and the master on page 110 to plan comprehension checks for English Learners.

English Proficiency	Prompts
Beginning	*Point to the pictures of your number story in order.*
Early Intermediate	*Where does your number story take place?*
Intermediate	*Tell your number story.*

Providing Access: Role-Playing

Role-playing provides children with language practice while they learn new math concepts. In this lesson, children role-play shopping and making change. Brainstorm scenarios between shopkeepers and shoppers and phrases they might say, including "You're welcome," "How may I help you?" and "How much is this?"

Previewing Vocabulary

An explanation of words with multiple meanings, key math terms, and common procedural vocabulary may aid student comprehension. Consider previewing these terms and reinforcing them as they are used in the lesson.

Words and Phrases	Meanings
storekeeper, page 700	A person who runs or manages a small store may be called a *storekeeper* or *shopkeeper*.
shopper, page 700	A person who shops, or looks for things to buy, is a shopper.
making change, page 700	Accepting payment and giving the shopper back the change or extra money that was paid for something is making change.

Building Academic Language: Words with Multiple Meanings

English has many words that have multiple meanings. For instance, English Learners may be confused by the subtle differences between *making change* and *making a change*. List the ways the word *change* is used and have English Learners draw a symbol or clue next to each use to help them remember the meaning.

Checking for Understanding

Use the prompts below, your own questions, and the master on page 110 to plan comprehension checks for English Learners.

English Proficiency	Prompts
Beginning	*I want to buy a ticket for 50 cents. Show how you would make change for a dollar.*
Early Intermediate	*If I want to buy two tickets for 50 cents each, will I need 1 dollar or 2 dollars to pay?*
Intermediate	*Describe three ways you can make change for a dollar if I buy 1 ticket for 50 cents.*

Equal Shares

Providing Access: Building a Math Word Bank

Encourage English Learners to create and add to a Math Word Bank. Children can collect both math terms and other new words on this master. Have them write the word, draw a picture or symbol for the word, and add other words, including words in their home language, to help them better understand its meaning. Use the template on page 109 of this handbook.

Previewing Vocabulary

An explanation of words with multiple meanings, key math terms, and common procedural vocabulary may aid student comprehension. Consider previewing these terms and reinforcing them as they are used in the lesson.

Words and Phrases	Meanings
jam, page 706	This word has multiple meanings, but here, it means a fruit spread, similar to jelly. Show a picture or the actual item.
scoop, page 708	(v.) To scrape, dig, or shovel something is to scoop it.
empty, page 708	(v.) In this context, the word *empty* is an action. To *empty* something means to take everything out so nothing is left.

Building Academic Language: Expanding Vocabulary

In this lesson, children "make" jam sandwiches. Colored squares represent the different foods. Review these foods and their names with all children since they may be unfamiliar with the bread, crackers, and different types of jam used in the activity.

Checking for Understanding

Use the prompts below, your own questions, and the master on page 110 to plan comprehension checks for English Learners.

English Proficiency	Prompts
Beginning	*Cut the cracker into three equal parts. Show that they are equal.*
Early Intermediate	*Which is easier to divide into equal parts, a sheet of paper or a cracker?*
Intermediate	*Is it possible to divide a real cracker into three equal parts? Why?*

Fractions

Providing Access: Connecting Concepts to Everyday Life

In this lesson, children begin to work with fraction notation. To reinforce the concept that fractions are always part of a whole, have English Learners look around the classroom for objects divided into equal parts, such as the floor or ceiling. Count up the number of parts in an item. Have children point to one or more of those parts and record the fraction notation on the board.

Previewing Vocabulary

An explanation of words with multiple meanings, key math terms, and common procedural vocabulary may aid student comprehension. Consider previewing these terms and reinforcing them as they are used in the lesson.

Words and Phrases	Meanings
quarter-sheet, page 711	If a page is divided into four equal parts, one part is a quarter-sheet. Emphasize that a quarter-sheet is one-fourth of a sheet.
How do you know?, page 712	Restate this question as "What proof do you have?" or "What information gives you the answer and helps you know it is correct?"

Building Academic Language: Idiomatic Expressions

As children discuss whether a glass is half full or half empty, share that a person with a positive outlook on life is described as a person who sees the glass as half full. There is still more left. A person who sees the glass as half empty is described as a person who has a negative outlook. Half of the contents are gone. Both are correct ways of judging the amount of water, but are different outlooks or perspectives.

Checking for Understanding

Use the prompts below, your own questions, and the master on page 110 to plan comprehension checks for English Learners.

English Proficiency	Prompts
Beginning	*Point to a half-sheet of paper. Point to a quarter-sheet of paper.*
Early Intermediate	*Name two ways to describe a quarter-sheet of paper.*
Intermediate	*Why is 25 cents called a quarter?*

Sharing Pennies

Providing Access: Role-Playing

In this lesson, children practice sharing pennies equally with others. Review what *equal* means by modeling sharing the pennies equally and then unequally. Have children act out sharing 12 pennies equally among 3 people. Role-playing reinforces the concept and gives English Learners practice using the related language.

Previewing Vocabulary

An explanation of words with multiple meanings, key math terms, and common procedural vocabulary may aid student comprehension. Consider previewing these terms and reinforcing them as they are used in the lesson.

Words and Phrases	Meanings
piles, page 715	A pile is like a stack but is less organized. A pile of objects is a number of items lying on top of one another, for example, a pile of clothes.
run out of pennies, page 715	Explain that when you have counted out all the pennies, you run out. You do not have any more left to share.

Building Academic Language: Nontransferable Skill—/th/

In this lesson, children work with halves, thirds, and fourths. English Learners may not have words in their primary language that end with /th/ and may find it difficult to distinguish this ending in English. They may approximate the sound by using a /s/ or other sound. Point out this ending in fractions, such as *one-fourth,* and articulate it carefully so children can distinguish when fractions are being used.

Checking for Understanding

Use the prompts below, your own questions, and the master on page 110 to plan comprehension checks for English Learners.

English Proficiency	Prompts
Beginning	*Show $\frac{1}{4}$ of 12 pennies.*
Early Intermediate	*Is this $\frac{1}{2}$ or $\frac{1}{3}$?*
Intermediate	*Share your 12 pennies equally with one other person. Explain how to do that.*

Explorations: Exploring Fractional Parts and Addition Facts

Providing Access: Hands-on Models

An excellent way to check for understanding with English Learners of limited English proficiency is to provide hands-on models. Using models allows children to demonstrate their understanding without relying heavily on their English skills. Have children demonstrate different fractional parts of regions on a geoboard.

Previewing Vocabulary

An explanation of words with multiple meanings, key math terms, and common procedural vocabulary may aid student comprehension. Consider previewing these terms and reinforcing them as they are used in the lesson.

Words and Phrases	Meanings
record sheet, page 721	A paper to write down or record information on is a record sheet.
near doubles, page 722	English Learners may know the everyday meaning of *near* as physically close, as in "I sit near her." In this context, *near* means "almost" in these phrases: *near perfect, near miss,* and *near doubles.*
two-fisted, page 723	Explain that when you fold in your fingers, you form a fist. *Two-fisted* means to form fists with both hands like when you grab pennies in *Two-Fisted Penny Addition*.

Building Academic Language: Imperative Form

Class rules and directions are often given in the command form of English, called the *imperative*. "Wait," "Stop," and "Listen" are examples. In this lesson, children work with geoboards and rubber bands to show fractional parts of regions. Brainstorm together rules for this activity and write them out for children. For example, "Keep rubber bands on the desk." You may want to accompany the rules with a picture.

Checking for Understanding

Use the prompts below, your own questions, and the master on page 110 to plan comprehension checks for English Learners.

English Proficiency	Prompts
Beginning	*Write three examples of near doubles.*
Early Intermediate	*Name three examples of near doubles.*
Intermediate	*What are near doubles?*

Tens and Ones Patterns on the Number Grid

Providing Access: Reinforcing Concepts with Movement

Discuss a number pattern found on the number grid, such as 0s in the ones place. Use a pointer to count with children on the Number-Grid Poster. Emphasize the pattern and reinforce the key concept. Each time children say a number that has 0 in the ones place, have them perform a gross-motor movement, such as a jumping jack.

Previewing Vocabulary

An explanation of words with multiple meanings, key math terms, and common procedural vocabulary may aid student comprehension. Consider previewing these terms and reinforcing them as they are used in the lesson.

Words and Phrases	Meanings
belongs, page 744	To belong is to be a member of a group. For example, "An apple belongs to the fruit group."
hidden, page 744	Something hidden is not seen because something is covering it up.
missing numbers, page 744	*Missing* refers to something that needs to be found. The numbers needed to complete a number sentence or pattern are the missing numbers.

Building Academic Language: Prepositions

Prepositions can be challenging to English Learners. Working on the number grid gives English Learners many opportunities to practice giving directions using location words. Brainstorm with the class prepositions they can use to give directions, including *before, after, next to, above, across,* and *beside.*

Checking for Understanding

Use the prompts below, your own questions, and the master on page 110 to plan comprehension checks for English Learners.

English Proficiency	Prompts
Beginning	*Show the number that comes after 10.*
Early Intermediate	*Which number comes after 10?*
Intermediate	*What is another way to describe the number that comes after 10?*

Adding and Subtracting Tens

Providing Access: Cultural Note

In this lesson, children tally how many letters they have in their first names. Do a quick review of the American tradition for naming so that English Learners know what is meant by *first name, last name,* and *middle name.* Some children may have two last names, including the mother's family name and the father's family name.

Previewing Vocabulary

An explanation of words with multiple meanings, key math terms, and common procedural vocabulary may aid student comprehension. Consider previewing these terms and reinforcing them as they are used in the lesson.

Words and Phrases	Meanings
roll a die, page 749	To gently toss one of a pair of dice is to roll a die.
forward/backward, page 752	Explain that forward is the direction that you see when you look ahead; you face forward. Backward is the direction behind you.
shortcut, page 752	A route or a way to arrive some place that takes less time or distance is a shortcut. You cut short part of the distance or time.

Building Academic Language: Nontransferable Skill—/z/

The letter *s* has several pronunciations. It has the voiceless /s/ sound as in *pass* and *cats* or the voiced /z/ as in the words *rows* and *tens.* Make a two-column chart and collect words that end with each of these sounds. Point out any patterns in words that have the voiceless /s/ sound.

Checking for Understanding

Use the prompts below, your own questions, and the master on page 110 to plan comprehension checks for English Learners.

English Proficiency	Prompts
Beginning	*Write your first name.*
Early Intermediate	*What is your first name?*
Intermediate	*Name the first and last name of another person who has the same first name as you.*

Number-Grid Puzzles

Providing Access: Practicing with Games

In this lesson, children practice naming and describing geometric figures and spatial relationships by playing *Make My Design*. Players take turns giving each other directions on how to create a figure relying only on verbal directions. Brainstorm location words and verbal directions for children to use.

Previewing Vocabulary

An explanation of words with multiple meanings, key math terms, and common procedural vocabulary may aid student comprehension. Consider previewing these terms and reinforcing them as they are used in the lesson.

Words and Phrases	Meanings
cells, page 754	Each box in the number grid is called a cell.
empty, page 755	*Empty* means there is nothing inside. An empty cell has no numbers in it.
hints, page 757	Clues, little bits of information that help a person guess the correct answer, are hints.

Building Academic Language: Hard and Soft *c*

In English, the letter *c* makes different sounds depending on the letters that surround it. English Learners who speak Spanish are familiar with the hard and soft *c*. It is a transferable skill from Spanish to English. Create or add to a chart to show the different sounds:

Hard *c* sounds like /k/ when followed by *a, o,* or *u*.	Soft *c* sounds like /s/ when followed by *e, i,* or *y*.
can	cell
code	circle
count	pieces
cut	place

Checking for Understanding

Use the prompts below, your own questions, and the master on page 110 to plan comprehension checks for English Learners.

English Proficiency	Prompts
Beginning	*Cover the number 13 on the number grid.*
Early Intermediate	*Which numbers are covered by the T-piece?*
Intermediate	*Give directions to find numbers with 5 in the ones place on the number grid.*

Lesson 9·4 Adding and Subtracting 2-Digit Numbers

Providing Access: Using Physical Models

Enhance comprehension of number stories by having English Learners use base-10 blocks to model the number stories in this lesson. Review how to use the base-10 blocks to represent various aspects of the story and make the necessary exchanges. Look back to Lesson 5.5 in the *Teacher's Lesson Guide* for examples.

Previewing Vocabulary

An explanation of words with multiple meanings, key math terms, and common procedural vocabulary may aid student comprehension. Consider previewing these terms and reinforcing them as they are used in the lesson.

Words and Phrases	Meanings
suppose, page 759	To imagine, pretend, or think "What would happen if?" is to suppose.
nose to nose, page 759	Two things that are nose to nose are touching. Here, children imagine two animals lying down nose to nose in order to measure them.

Building Academic Language: Standard Questions

Because the words *length*, *width*, and *height* look different from *long*, *wide*, and *tall*, English Learners should practice the questions associated with common measurements. Make a chart with these question starters:

Measurement	Question	Description
Length	How long?	Length is the measurement of something from one end to the other.
Height	How tall?	Height is how tall someone or something is.

Checking for Understanding

Use the prompts below, your own questions, and the master on page 110 to plan comprehension checks for English Learners.

English Proficiency	Prompts
Beginning	*How tall are you?*
Early Intermediate	*Would you describe a basketball backboard as tall or long?*
Intermediate	*How do you measure someone's height?*

Explorations: Exploring Capacity, Symmetry, and Heights

Providing Access: Hands-on Examples

The concept of symmetry can be very difficult to explain using only words and even harder for English Learners to understand without examples. In this lesson, children use pattern blocks to create mirror images and better understand lines of symmetry and symmetrical figures.

Previewing Vocabulary

An explanation of words with multiple meanings, key math terms, and common procedural vocabulary may aid student comprehension. Consider previewing these terms and reinforcing them as they are used in the lesson.

Words and Phrases	Meanings
mirror image, page 765	A reflection of an image, an exact copy of an image as seen in a mirror is a mirror image.
unpainted, page 766	Something with no paint on it is unpainted.
outline the designs, page 766	(v.) To trace around the outside of a figure is to outline the design.

Building Academic Language: Cognates

Mathematics is rich with terminology rooted in Greek and Latin. English Learners who speak a language that shares these roots may benefit from reviewing cognates or related words. For example, words that end with -*ty* in English share a common root with Spanish words ending in -*dad*: *capacity/ capacidad*, *variety/variedad*, and *university/universidad*. Have children list other English words that end with -*ty*.

Checking for Understanding

Use the prompts below, your own questions, and the master on page 110 to plan comprehension checks for English Learners.

English Proficiency	Prompts
Beginning	*Show a symmetrical design.*
Early Intermediate	*Is this the line of symmetry?*
Intermediate	*What does it mean to say that things are symmetrical?*

Fractional Parts of the Whole

Providing Access: Connecting Concepts to Everyday Life

When introducing the concept of fractions, food is often used as an example because it provides authentic purposes for breaking apart a whole item. Tying new concepts to familiar experiences strengthens the connection of concepts and increases the likelihood of comprehension. Brainstorm with children other common examples of breaking apart a whole into fractional parts. List these items for English Learners to illustrate.

Previewing Vocabulary

An explanation of words with multiple meanings, key math terms, and common procedural vocabulary may aid student comprehension. Consider previewing these terms and reinforcing them as they are used in the lesson.

Words and Phrases	Meanings
come up with, page 769	This expression means to think of a way to solve a problem.
pretend, page 770	To play or imagine is to pretend.
stand for, page 770	This phrase is another way to say "represents" or "means."

Building Academic Language: Nouns, Adjectives, and Verbs

In this lesson, children shade and name fractional parts for shapes. Point out that the word *shade* is used here as an action and to describe something. Keep a wall word chart of such multiple-use words.

VERBS are actions.	NOUNS name a person, place, or thing.	ADJECTIVES describe nouns.
[to] label	[a] label	labeled
[to] shade	[the] shade	shaded

Checking for Understanding

Use the prompts below, your own questions, and the master on page 110 to plan comprehension checks for English Learners.

English Proficiency	Prompts
Beginning	*Who is the tallest person in your class?*
Early Intermediate	*Who is taller, you or the teacher?*
Intermediate	*Are there any children who are the same height?*

Comparing Fractions

Providing Access: Cognates

Mathematics is rich with terminology rooted in Greek and Latin. English Learners who speak a language that shares these roots may benefit from discussing cognates or related words. Words that end with *-or* in English are cognates with Spanish words, such as *numerator/numerador* and *denominator/denominador*. Single syllable *-or* words like *for* do not fit this pattern. Have children list English words that use the *-or* pattern.

Previewing Vocabulary

An explanation of words with multiple meanings, key math terms, and common procedural vocabulary may aid student comprehension. Consider previewing these terms and reinforcing them as they are used in the lesson.

Words and Phrases	Meanings
bottom, page 775	The lowest part is the bottom part.
dashed lines, page 776	Straight lines that are broken are sometimes called *dotted* or *dashed lines*.
facedown, page 777	Explain that when you lie on your stomach, your face is down and people cannot tell who you are. When a number card is facedown, the side with the numbers is not showing.

Building Academic Language: Nontransferable Skill—/th/

English Learners who do not have words in their primary language that end with /th/ may find it difficult to distinguish this ending sound in English. In this lesson, children learn that fraction words such as *fourths*, *sixths*, and *eighths* indicate the number of equal parts. Spanish speakers may approximate the /th/ sound by using a /s/, /t/, or other sound. Articulate /th/ carefully and point out this ending because it is critical to the concept of fractions.

Checking for Understanding

Use the prompts below, your own questions, and the master on page 110 to plan comprehension checks for English Learners.

English Proficiency	Prompts
Beginning	Show $\frac{1}{3}$ piece of paper. Show $\frac{1}{4}$ piece of paper. Point to the larger piece of paper.
Early Intermediate	Which is larger, $\frac{1}{3}$ or $\frac{1}{4}$ of a piece of paper?
Intermediate	How can you tell which fraction is bigger?

Many Names for Fractional Parts

Providing Access: Modeling Concepts

English Learners greatly benefit from demonstrating a new concept rather than simply talking about it. In this lesson, the concept of equivalent fractions is clarified through modeling. Children cover strips of paper with fraction pieces to determine which pieces can be combined to equal a given fraction.

Previewing Vocabulary

An explanation of words with multiple meanings, key math terms, and common procedural vocabulary may aid student comprehension. Consider previewing these terms and reinforcing them as they are used in the lesson.

Words and Phrases	Meanings
strips, page 779	Long, narrow pieces of paper are strips.
exchange, page 781	English Learners may know the word *change*. The word *exchange* is related. Each side gives and gets something in an exchange.

Building Academic Language: Silent *w*

In this lesson, children review that fractions are parts of a whole. The word *whole* is a homophone that may be confused with *hole*. Help English Learners recognize the difference and point out that the word *whole* is distinguished by its spelling of a silent *w* that marks the meaning of a complete *whole*.

Checking for Understanding

Use the prompts below, your own questions, and the master on page 110 to plan comprehension checks for English Learners.

English Proficiency	Prompts
Beginning	*Cover the $\frac{1}{2}$ fraction piece with $\frac{1}{8}$ pieces.*
Early Intermediate	*How many $\frac{1}{6}$ pieces are needed to cover the $\frac{1}{3}$ piece?*
Intermediate	*Give an example of equivalent fractions.*

Data Day: End-of-Year Heights

Providing Access: Practicing Questions

Since children are often asked questions rather than initiating questions themselves, it is important to give English Learners practice asking questions. Review questions for finding out someone's height and write them on the board. Read the questions aloud and model the inflection used in posing a question. Have English Learners survey classmates after they have been measured to practice asking questions.

Previewing Vocabulary

An explanation of words with multiple meanings, key math terms, and common procedural vocabulary may aid student comprehension. Consider previewing these terms and reinforcing them as they are used in the lesson.

Words and Phrases	Meanings
end-of-the-year heights, page 801	This phrase means the heights of children at the end of the school year. Explain that the school year is not the same as the calendar year.
over and over, page 802	This expression means to repeat many times.
halfway between, page 802	At the middle place between two things is halfway between.

Building Academic Language: Formulating Questions

Children will be asked for their age, height, and weight in many situations. Help English Learners know the associated questions for each measurement. Say: *When we ask someone's age, we say "How old are you?" When we ask someone's weight, we say "How much do you weigh?" When we ask someone's height, we do not say "How high are you?" We say "How tall are you?"* Remind children that it is considered impolite to ask an adult his or her age and that most people do not like to be asked their weight.

Checking for Understanding

Use the prompts below, your own questions, and the master on page 110 to plan comprehension checks for English Learners.

English Proficiency	Prompts
Beginning	*Show how tall you are. Write your height in feet and inches.*
Early Intermediate	*Is typical the same as average?*
Intermediate	*How do you ask a person what their height is?*

Review: Telling Time

Providing Access: Practicing Language in Authentic Settings

In everyday conversation, clock time may be read in several different ways. Use the class schedule to practice reading the time at the start and end of class and breaks. Discuss the different ways to say the time. For example, 3:05 is sometimes read, "three-oh-five." In this case, the number zero may be interpreted as the letter *o*. Discuss other ways to read 3:05, such as "five past three," or "five minutes after three."

Previewing Vocabulary

An explanation of words with multiple meanings, key math terms, and common procedural vocabulary may aid student comprehension. Consider previewing these terms and reinforcing them as they are used in the lesson.

Words and Phrases	Meanings
telling time, page 806	To look at the clock and say the hour and minutes is called *telling time*.
clock face, page 807	The flat surface of the clock that has the numbers on it is the clock face.
hands, page 807	On an analog clock, the short pointer that moves most slowly is the hour hand. It points to the hour on the clock and changes position every hour. The long pointer is the minute hand.

Building Academic Language: The Colon

Tell children that to write the time, you separate the hour from the minutes with a punctuation sign called a *colon*. The number before the colon stands for the hour. The numbers after the colon stands for minutes after the hour. Throughout the day, ask children to record the time.

Checking for Understanding

Use the prompts below, your own questions, and the master on page 110 to plan comprehension checks for English Learners.

English Proficiency	Prompts
Beginning	*Write the number of minutes in an hour.*
Early Intermediate	*How many minutes are in an hour?*
Intermediate	*What does a quarter-hour mean?*

Mental Arithmetic: Using a Vending Machine Poster

Providing Access: Connecting to Everyday Situations

Vending machines, snack bars, and other concessions collect large amounts of coins. To take coins to the bank or to use them more efficiently, shopkeepers often roll like coins together. Practice rolling pennies using penny wrappers from the bank. Ask: *How many pennies go into each roll?* Discuss why these are standardized amounts.

Previewing Vocabulary

An explanation of words with multiple meanings, key math terms, and common procedural vocabulary may aid student comprehension. Consider previewing these terms and reinforcing them as they are used in the lesson.

Words and Phrases	Meanings
purchase, page 812	(v.) Another word for *buy* is *purchase*. Here, purchase is an action.
vending machine, page 812	A machine for selling small items is a vending machine. A vendor is a person who sells things.
random, page 815	Things that are unplanned, left to chance, are random.

Building Academic Language: Changing Verbs to Nouns

One way to talk about people who do a job is to add *-er* to the end of the action. For example, a person who wins is a winner. A person who runs is a runner. By adding *-er* to the action, the name is formed. In this lesson, a person who sells is a seller and a person who buys is a buyer. Make a chart of job titles that fit this pattern and have children add to it: *A person who ____ is a ____.*

Checking for Understanding

Use the prompts below, your own questions, and the master on page 110 to plan comprehension checks for English Learners.

English Proficiency	Prompts
Beginning	*Does your school sell lunches?*
Early Intermediate	*What do we call a person who buys things?*
Intermediate	*Tell what a teacher does. Tell what a swimmer does. What does a vendor do?*

Providing Access: Role-Playing

English Learners deepen their understanding of money when they act out number stories about making change, using real or tool-kit coins. Have English Learners work in small groups to discuss each number story and determine how to demonstrate the action and what dialogue to use.

Previewing Vocabulary

An explanation of words with multiple meanings, key math terms, and common procedural vocabulary may aid student comprehension. Consider previewing these terms and reinforcing them as they are used in the lesson.

Words and Phrases	Meanings
enough money, page 818	If you have the amount of money to pay for a purchase, you have enough money.
... will he get back?, page 818	This phrase is used in the question "How much money will he get back?" It asks what will he receive in return as change.
pool their money, page 819	Explain that when players pool their money, they combine their money together.

Building Academic Language: Plurals

Not all languages add an affix, such as - *s,* to make a noun plural. In some languages, the number name tells the listener that the noun is plural. When English Learners transfer their grammar to English, it can result in errors in plural forms. You might hear a child say "Two dime and three penny." Post a plural chart and discuss.

Add -s to the End	Add -es to the End	Words that Change	Collective Nouns
bill: bills	guess: guesses	die: dice	change: some change
nickel: nickels	penny: pennies	half: halves	money: some money

Checking for Understanding

Use the prompts below, your own questions, and the master on page 110 to plan comprehension checks for English Learners.

English Proficiency	Prompts
Beginning	*Show me a $10 bill.*
Early Intermediate	*Is this a coin or a bill?*
Intermediate	*Tell which is easier to carry, $10 in coins or $10 in bills.*

Year-End Geometry Review

Providing Access: Playing Games

Playing games gives English Learners authentic language and skills practice through repetition. In this lesson, the word game *I Spy* is introduced. Explain the meaning of the word *spy* and how it is used here. Practice together the refrain, *I spy with my little eye, _____.* Before playing the game, brainstorm a list of attributes that describe the shapes.

Previewing Vocabulary

An explanation of words with multiple meanings, key math terms, and common procedural vocabulary may aid student comprehension. Consider previewing these terms and reinforcing them as they are used in the lesson.

Words and Phrases	Meanings
polygons are made up of …, page 823	Here, *made up* means to consist of. Restate the phrase as, "polygons have …"
gaps, page 823	Small spaces between two objects that typically should touch each other are called *gaps*.
match, page 824	Explain that to match numbers or objects, you pair up two objects that share some characteristics.

Building Academic Language: Cognates

Mathematics is rich with terminology rooted in Greek and Latin. Spanish speakers will find many words that are shared across English and Spanish. Geometric figures that end with *-angle* in English, such as *triangle,* end with *-ángulo* in Spanish, as in *triángulo.* Those that end with *-gon* in English, such as *polygon,* end with *-gono* in Spanish, as in *polígono.* Throughout this lesson, collect other examples in a two-column chart headed *-angle/-ángulo* and *-gon/-gono.*

Checking for Understanding

Use the prompts below, your own questions, and the master on page 110 to plan comprehension checks for English Learners.

English Proficiency	Prompts
Beginning	*Show me an octagon. Point to the faces, sides, corners …*
Early Intermediate	*What is the name of a polygon with 8 sides of the same length?*
Intermediate	*Compare a pentagon and an octagon. How are they alike? How are they different?*

Review: Thermometers and Temperature

Providing Access: Tapping Prior Knowledge

English Learners often need to rely on others to help them understand the instruction and practice in school each day. Working with temperature presents an excellent opportunity for English Learners to share their expertise with the group. Children who have lived outside the United States may be more familiar with the Celsius scale. Explore this potential asset in your class and utilize any Celsius scale experts.

Previewing Vocabulary

An explanation of words with multiple meanings, key math terms, and common procedural vocabulary may aid student comprehension. Consider previewing these terms and reinforcing them as they are used in the lesson.

Words and Phrases	Meanings
outdoor, page 829	Outside of any buildings in the open air is called the *outdoors*.
forecast, page 829	A weather prediction that tells what the weather and temperature in the near future might be is a forecast.
daily, page 829	Something done daily is done every day.

Building Academic Language: Talking about the Weather

As English Learners work with temperatures, review basic questions and expressions about the weather. Let children know that sometimes people talk about the weather when they begin a conversation. The weather is easy to talk about because it is a shared experience. People might say, "How do you like this weather?" or "Is it hot enough for you?"

Checking for Understanding

Use the prompts below, your own questions, and the master on page 110 to plan comprehension checks for English Learners.

English Proficiency	Prompts
Beginning	*Show a temperature on a hot day on the thermometer.*
Early Intermediate	*Which is warmer, 45°C or 45°F?*
Intermediate	*What is today's temperature outdoors in both Celsius and Fahrenheit scales?*

Review: Place Value, Scrolls, and Number Grids

Providing Access: Hands-on Examples

Everyday Mathematics integrates the use of hands-on modeling, which provides scaffolding for English Learners. Children can demonstrate their understanding as they work to learn the academic language. Using hands-on materials reinforces concepts through active participation.

Previewing Vocabulary

An explanation of words with multiple meanings, key math terms, and common procedural vocabulary may aid student comprehension. Consider previewing these terms and reinforcing them as they are used in the lesson.

Words and Phrases	Meanings
exchange, page 833	English Learners may know the word *change*. The word *exchange* is related. Each side gives and gets something in an exchange.
trade, page 834	*Trade* means to give something and get something of equal value in return. A trade is an exchange.
cells, page 835	The boxes in the number grid are called *cells*. In order to avoid confusion, point out that the word *cells* begins with a *c*, which is a homophone with *sells*.

Building Academic Language: Nontransferable Skill—Initial /scr/ and /str/

English Learners may find initial consonant clusters very challenging if those same consonant clusters do not exist or are not used in initial positions in their home language. For example, Spanish speakers will often add a vowel to the beginning of *scroll* or *straw*. Model the articulation carefully and provide brief practice with the pronunciation of each word.

Checking for Understanding

Use the prompts below, your own questions, and the master on page 110 to plan comprehension checks for English Learners.

English Proficiency	Prompts
Beginning	*Point to the largest number on your number scroll.*
Early Intermediate	*What is the largest number on your number scroll?*
Intermediate	*How many more numbers will you include on your number scroll?*

Math Word Bank

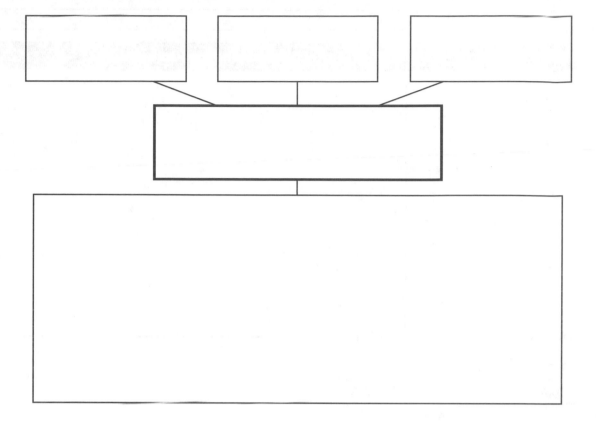

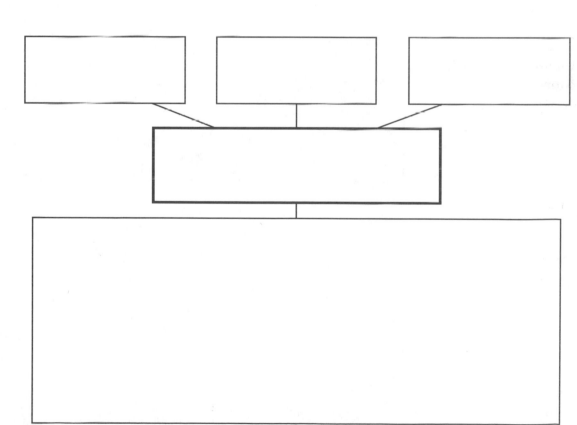

Planning Master

Lesson _____

English Proficiency	Checking for Understanding Prompts
Beginning ◆ Thumbs-up/ thumbs-down… ◆ Nod your head yes/no… ◆ Show me… ◆ Point to the… ◆ Illustrate…	
Early Intermediate ◆ Either _____ or _____ ◆ Give a one-word answer or short answer ◆ Make a list… ◆ Complete a sentence frame or template ◆ Complete a graphic organizer	
Intermediate ◆ Compare/contrast ◆ Describe… ◆ Sequence… ◆ How…? or Why…? (open-ended questions)	